KT-460-552

MATHS
IN ACTION
PLUS

AUTHORS

R. Howat	Adviser, Ayr
G. Marra	Linlathen High School, Dundee
E. Mullan	Galashiels Academy
R. Murray	Hawick High School
J. Thomson	Galashiels Academy

CALDERVALE HIGH SCHOOL
TOWERS ROAD
AIRDRIE
ML6 8PG

STUDENTS' BOOK

Thomas Nelson and Sons Ltd
Nelson House Mayfield Road
Walton-on-Thames Surrey
KT12 5PL UK

Cover photograph courtesy of Rolls Royce

© R. Howat, G. Marra, E. Mullan, R. Murray and J. Thomson 1996

First published by Thomas Nelson and Sons Ltd 1996
I Ⓣ P Thomas Nelson is an International Thomson Publishing Company
I Ⓣ P is used under licence

ISBN 0–17–431456–6
NPN 9 8 7 6 5 4

All rights reserved. No paragraph of this publication may be reproduced,
copied or transmitted save with written permission or in accordance with
the provisions of the Copyright, Design and Patents Act 1988, or under the
terms of any licence permitting limited copying issued by the Copyright
Licensing Agency, 90 Tottenham Court Road, London W1P 9HE.

Any person who does any unauthorised act in relation to this publication
may be liable to criminal prosecution and civil claims for damages.

Printed in China

CONTENTS

Note: the 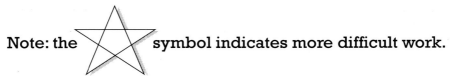 symbol indicates more difficult work.

1 WHOLE NUMBERS AND DECIMALS

Calculating devices are useful but they may not always be there when you need them.

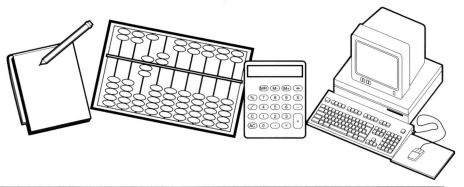

LOOKING BACK

1 a 24 + 35   **b** 84 − 36   **c** 7 × 8   **d** 32 ÷ 4

2 a 4 × 10   **b** 4 × 100   **c** 32 × 10   **d** 32 × 100

3 a 1000 ÷ 10   **b** 1000 ÷ 100   **c** 200 ÷ 10   **d** 200 ÷ 100

> **Examples a** $3.65 \times 10 = 36.5$ **b** $14.7 \div 10 = 1.47$

4 a 8.79 × 10   **b** 23.6 ÷ 10

5 a 8.79 × 100   **b** 23.6 ÷ 100

6

These four cards can be arranged to form 4-figure numbers.

a What is the **largest** number the four cards can form?
b What is the **smallest** number the four cards can form?
c Write your answers as words.

7 The number 265.34 has been entered in the table opposite.

a (i) What does **H** stand for?
   (ii) Write down the meaning of **T**, **U**, **t** and **h**.

b Copy the table. Enter the following numbers.
   (i) 809.56   (ii) 28.32   (iii) 372.05
   (iv) 9.8   (v) 3.6   (vi) 519

	H	T	U	t	h
	2	6	5	3	4
(i)					
(ii)					
(iii)					
(iv)					
(v)					
(vi)					

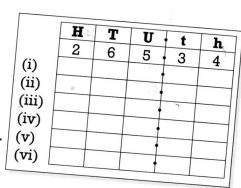

8 a $28.3 + 3.6$ **b** $19.35 + 306.4$ **c** $43 + 9.2$ **d** $13.7 - 6.8$
   e 3.2×4 **f** 1.26×5 **g** $8.46 \div 3$ **h** $8.05 \div 5$

9

> **Example 1** 68 is between 60 and 70.
> It is nearer 70.
> Rounded to the nearest 10,
> 68 becomes 70.

> **Example 2** 61 is between 60 and 70.
> It is nearer 60.
> Rounded to the nearest 10,
> 61 becomes 60.

> **Example 3** 65 is halfway between 60 and 70.
> We round it up.
> To the nearest 10,
> 65 becomes 70.

Round these numbers to the nearest 10.
   a 24   **b** 47   **c** 88   **d** 85   **e** 76

10

> **Examples** To the nearest 10
>   **a** 287 becomes 290
>   **b** 282 becomes 280
>   **c** 285 becomes 290.

Round these numbers to the nearest 10.
   a 368   **b** 572   **c** 193   **d** 945   **e** 786

Calculation Rules

BODMAS

When you have a string of calculations you must do them in a special order.

Example: $33 - 4 \times (5 - 2) + 5$

(B) Are there any brackets?	$33 - 4 \times 3 + 5$
(O) Does the word 'of' appear? In this case, no.	$33 - 4 \times 3 + 5$
(DM) Are there any $\div$ or $\times$?	$33 - 12 + 5$
(AS) Do any $+$ or $-$ from left to right.	$21 + 5 = 26$

 See if your calculator follows the rules.

EXERCISE 1

1 a $4 + 5 \times 3$ **b** $1 + 6 \times 2$ **c** $12 - 3 \times 2$ **d** $20 - 4 \times 5$
   e $8 + 4 \div 2$ **f** $15 - 6 \div 3$ **g** $4 \times (2 + 3)$ **h** $4 \times 3 - 1$
   i $\frac{1}{2}$ of $6 + 4$ **j** $\frac{1}{2}$ of $(6 + 4)$ **k** $\frac{1}{2}$ of $(8 - 2)$ **l** $\frac{1}{2}$ of $8 - 2$

Now try the BODMAS Maze.

2 Copy and complete this cross-number puzzle.

1			2		3
		4			
		5		6	
	7				
8			9		10
		11			

Clues across
1 $1 + 2 + 3 + 4 + 5 +$
  $6 + 7 + 8 + 9 + 10$
2 $486 \div 3$
4 $10 \times 10 - 19$
5 $(10 - 6) + 20 \times 10$
7 $115 \div (3 + 2)$
8 $(32 - 27) \times 10$
9 $5 \times 5 \times 5$
11 $100 \times 10 - 967$

Clues down
1 $1000 - 445$
2 $(7 + 4) \times (12 - 2)$
3 $8 + 3 \times 5$
4 $428 + 395$
6 $6 \times 8 \times 9$
8 $1000 \div 5 \div 4$
10 $9 + 13 + 17 + 18$

Ordering Numbers

Example 1   Put 7, 1, 4, 2 in order, **highest** first.
Answer: 7, 4, 2, 1.
Example 2   Put 3.1, 3.6, 4.9, 3.9 in order, **lowest** first.
Answer: 3.1, 3.6, 3.9, 4.9.

EXERCISE 2

1 Sort each list out, **highest** first.
  a 8, 1, 4, 6, 5
  b 7, 3, 12, 26, 4
  c 2.6, 3.5, 7.2, 1.4
  d 16.4, 5.2, 29.3, 29.4

2 Sort each list out, **lowest** first.
  a 26, 17, 32, 19
  b 7.9, 18.4, 18.0, 25.2
  c 6.8, 14.9, 1.0, 0.1
  d 41.2, 40.0, 26.2, 14.3

3 a Key in the following on your calculator.
    (i) 4.2 =
    (ii) 4.20 =
    (iii) 4.200000 =

  b What do you notice?

> Adding zeros to the end of a decimal
> does not change its size.

4 Add zeros to the ends of some of these decimals so that each of them has the same number of figures after the point.
For example: 4.6, 4.58 becomes 4.60, 4.58.
Each number has two figures after the point.

    a 3.9, 3.06   **b** 17.5, 16.46   **c** 18.2, 18.165

5 Put each set of numbers in order, lowest first.
(Hint: add zeros as in question 4.)

    a 3.8, 3.09, 3.65   **b** 6.7, 6.71, 6.66   **c** 12.8, 12.42, 12.9

6 Six athletes ran the 100 m race.
Their times (in seconds) were:

10.8, 10.7, 10.68, 10.96, 11.2, 11.19.

Write this list out, lowest first.

Rounding

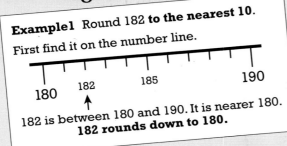

Example1 Round 182 **to the nearest 10**.
First find it on the number line.

180   182   185   190

182 is between 180 and 190. It is nearer 180.
182 rounds down to 180.

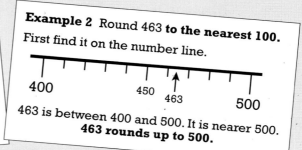

Example 2 Round 463 **to the nearest 100**.
First find it on the number line.

400   450   463   500

463 is between 400 and 500. It is nearer 500.
463 rounds up to 500.

Note: if a number falls halfway between two possibilities, then round up.

EXERCISE 3

1 Use the number line to help you round each of the following numbers to the **nearest 10**.

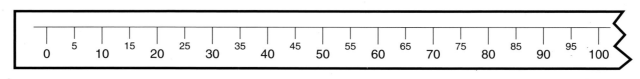

    a 88   **b** 71   **c** 16   **d** 25   **e** 69   **f** 93   **g** 34   **h** 53

Use this part of the number line to help you with **i-l**.

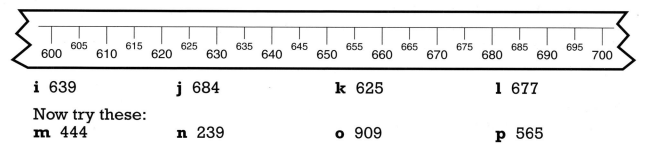

i 639   **j** 684   **k** 625   **l** 677

Now try these:

m 444   **n** 239   **o** 909   **p** 565

2 Use the number line to help you round each of the following numbers to the **nearest 100**.

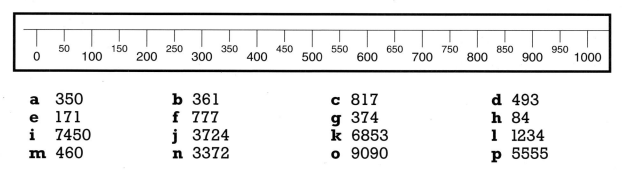

a 350	**b** 361	**c** 817	**d** 493
e 171	**f** 777	**g** 374	**h** 84
i 7450	**j** 3724	**k** 6853	**l** 1234
m 460	**n** 3372	**o** 9090	**p** 5555

3 Use the scales to help you round to the **nearest whole number**.

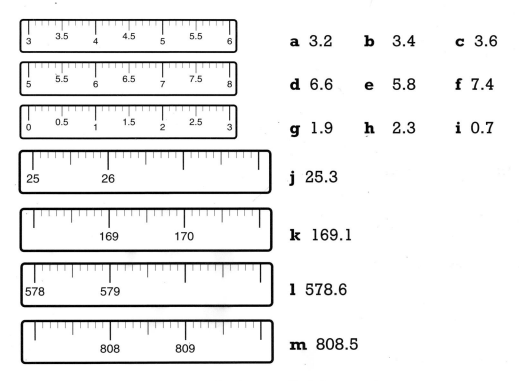

a 3.2   **b** 3.4   **c** 3.6

d 6.6   **e** 5.8   **f** 7.4

g 1.9   **h** 2.3   **i** 0.7

j 25.3

k 169.1

l 578.6

m 808.5

4 **a** Use your calculator to do these divisions.
   (i) 10.8 ÷ 3   (ii) 24.8 ÷ 4   (iii) 94.5 ÷ 7

b Round your answers to the nearest whole number.

Sharing

Sometimes the story in a question wants a whole number answer, but it won't let you round to the **nearest** whole number.

Example

A taxi can only carry 4 people.
How many taxis are needed to transport:
a 7 people **b** 5 people?

a 7 ÷ 4 = 1.75. We round this up to 2 taxis.
b 5 ÷ 4 = 1.25. We *still* round this up to 2 taxis.
We can't leave one person behind.

EXERCISE 4

1 The lift can safely carry 8 people.
How many trips will it make to get
25 people up to the third floor?

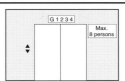

2 The school minibus can carry 12 passengers.
How many journeys will it need to make to transport
42 people to the leisure centre?

3 Six friends share £100 in a lottery.
a How much does each friend receive?
b How much money is left over?

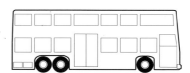

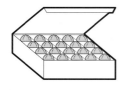

4 A box contains 40 chocolates.
Seven children are to have an equal share.
a How many chocolates does each child get?
b How many chocolates are left over?

5 Kirsty's car needs urgent repairs!
She needs to save at least £50 in six weeks.
What is the smallest amount she needs to save each week?

6 16 litres of paint are needed to treat a fence.
Paint is sold in 5 litre tins.
How many tins of paint do we need?

7 180 students and 12 teachers go on a trip.
a How many 56-seater buses are needed?
b How many empty seats will there be?

Reminder

Even and Odd Numbers

$0 \div 2 = 0$.
0 can be divided by 2, so 0 is even.
$8 \div 2 = 4$.
8 can be divided by 2, so 8 is even
$7 \div 2 = 3.5$.
7 cannot be divided by 2, so 7 is odd.

Prime Numbers

A prime number is bigger than 1 and it can only be divided by itself and 1.

2 and 3 are primes.
$4 \div 2 = 2$, so 4 is not a prime.
$15 \div 5 = 3$, so 15 is not a prime.

EXERCISE 5

1 a List the first ten even numbers. Start at zero.
b List the first ten odd numbers.

2 As we walk down a street the even numbered houses are on the right and the odd numbered houses are on the left.
On what side of the road will you find:
a 24 **b** 18 **c** 27 **d** 16 **e** 85 **f** 92 **g** 169 **h** 720?

3 2, 3, 5 and 7 are the first four prime numbers. List the next six.

4 a Use your calculator to help you find the primes in this list:
31, 34, 35, 37, 49, 51, 59, 61.
b '18 is not a prime because it can be divided by 6.'
Give a reason like this for all the numbers in the list which are *not prime*.

5 There are three safe trails for the explorer, Idaho Jones, to cross to the treasure. He can follow:
a even numbers only **b** primes only **c** odd numbers but avoid 43.

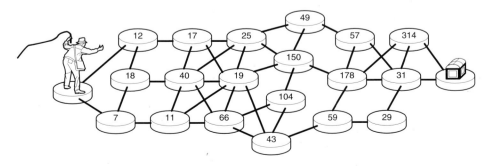

List the numbers on a safe trail of each type.

6 Adam and Bill play a game using two dice. The rules are given in the box.

Start with a total of zero.
If you throw:
- two odd numbers, add them together
- two even numbers, multiply them
- one odd and one even number, subtract them.
Add your score to your total.

Examples
(5, 1) scores 6.
(2, 4) scores 8.
(1, 6) scores 5.

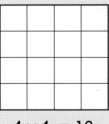

a What do the following throws score?
(i) (3, 3)   (ii) (2, 6)   (iii) (2, 5)

b Adam and Bill played a game. Here are their score cards.

Copy and complete the cards to see who won.

Name	Adam
Throw	Score
(1, 3)	4
(2, 5)	3
(4, 1)	3
(4, 4)	16
(3, 5)	
(1, 1)	
(4, 2)	
Total	

Name	Bill
Throw	Score
(6, 2)	12
(4, 3)	
(3, 1)	
(5, 2)	
(1, 3)	
(6, 2)	
(2, 2)	
Total	

c Play the game.
The player with the highest total after seven throws is the winner.

Square Numbers

A number multiplied by itself makes a square number.

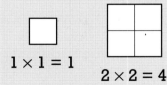

$1 \times 1 = 1$

$2 \times 2 = 4$

$3 \times 3 = 9$

$4 \times 4 = 16$

We often write: $1^2 = 1$ $2^2 = 4$ $3^2 = 9$ $4^2 = 16$
1, 4, 9 and 16 are the first four square numbers.

EXERCISE 6

1 Write down the next four square numbers.

2 Use your calculator to help you work out the following squares.
   a 10^2 **b** 15^2 **c** 25^2 **d** 1000^2 **e** 30^2 **f** 50^2 **g** 64^2

3 The calculator can help you spot which numbers are square numbers.

> **Example** √2 = 1.414213565, a decimal answer, so **2 is not a square**.
> √64 = 8, a whole number answer, so **64 is a square**. 8² = 64.

Show that 441 and 576 are squares.

4 Which of these numbers are square?
  a 144   **b** 900   **c** 300   **d** 189   **e** 400   **f** 500   **g** 625

5 Here is Idaho Jones again. Only the stones etched with a square number are safe.

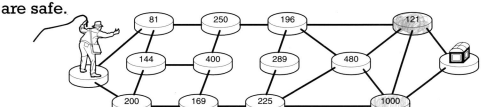

List the numbers which lie on the safe route to the treasure.

A Mixture of Examples

EXERCISE 7

1 Molly buys shampoo for £1.95 and conditioner for £1.69.
  a What is her total bill?
  b What change is she given from £5?

2 Julie is paid £3.50 an hour. She works 40 hours. How much does she earn?

3 Tom earns £138 for working 40 hours. How much is he paid an hour?

4 Greg studies the map. There are three routes from Afton to Bradon.
  a What is the length of the shortest route?
  b How long is the longest route?
  c What is the difference between the longest and shortest routes?

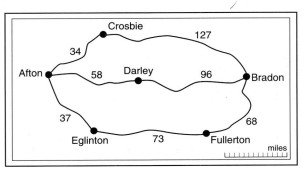

5

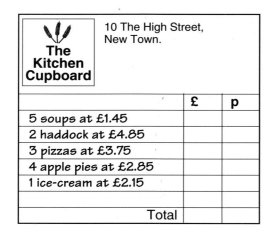

The Tuck family eat out.
Copy and complete their bill.

	£	p
5 soups at £1.45		
2 haddock at £4.85		
3 pizzas at £3.75		
4 apple pies at £2.85		
1 ice-cream at £2.15		
Total		

6 There were 846 735 visitors to the Kyle Leisure Centre last year.

Round this number off to:
a the nearest thousand
b the nearest hundred.

7 Hope collected money for charity.
When she checked it she found she had:

eighteen 1p coins, thirteen 2p coins, twenty-three 5p coins, thirty-five 10p coins, twenty-seven 20p coins, eleven 50p coins and seven £1 coins.

Copy and complete the pay-in slip.

Type	Number	Amount (p)
1p	18	18
2p	13	26
5p		
10p		
20p		
50p		
£1		
Total		£

8

Fair Store Price
18p each

Better Deal Price
£1 for a six-pack

Martin buys six cans of Quenchy from Fair Store.
Jill buys a six-pack from Better Deal.
a How much did Martin pay?
b How much less did Jill pay?

9 Tom, Sue and Bob have just won £23 840 325 in the Lottery.
They share it out equally.
a How much does each get?
b Tom buys a new home for his family. It costs him £280 000.
He gives away £3 million to friends.
He spends £110 000 on himself.
How much does he have left to put in the bank?

★ Star ★
Prize
LOTTERY
THE ROLLOVER JACKPOT IS
NOW ESTIMATED AT 36M
A. 01 03 07 09 13 49
B. 02 13 15 24 33 40
C. 04 11 15 22 29 49
D. 03 10 11 25 34 44
E. 05 16 19 32 33 41
Sat 27 Jan 96
For 01 Draw
010056   £ 5.00
★ ★ ★ ★ ★ ★

CHECK-UP ON WHOLE NUMBERS AND DECIMALS

1 Calculate: **a** $23.6 + 3.49$ **b** $26.54 - 18.6$ **c** 13.6×4 **d** $374.4 \div 4$

2 Calculate: **a** $3 + 4 \times 5$ **b** $15 - 3 \times 4$ **c** $5 \times (3 + 4)$ **d** $24 \div (4 + 2)$

3 Here are four numbers: $3, 12, 14.86, 7.4$.

Multiply each of them by: **a** 10 **b** 100

4 Here are another four numbers: $5000, 17\ 600, 376.8, 281$.

Divide each of them by: **a** 10 **b** 100

5 Round these numbers to the nearest 10.

a 68 **b** 43 **c** 25 **d** 136

6 Round these numbers to the nearest 100.

a 370 **b** 420 **c** 4680

7 There were 31 692 spectators at the City versus Rovers football match.

Give this figure to the nearest:
a thousand **b** hundred.

8 List these numbers in order, putting the biggest first:

$34.84, 35.01, 34.47, 35.6, 34.9, 35.48$.

9 Here are seven numbers: $2, 3, 36, 81, 90, 31, 49$.

From this list write down:

a three odd numbers
b three even numbers
c three prime numbers
d three square numbers.

10 How do you know:

a 15 is not a prime
b 100 is a square number
c 3452 is an even number?

2 SYMMETRY

LOOKING BACK

1 Which of the following shapes have line symmetry?

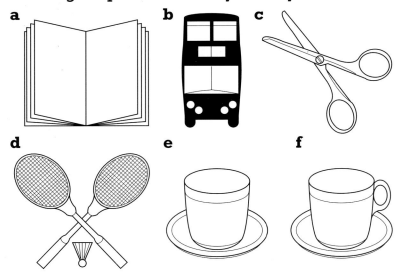

2 Copy these diagrams onto squared paper.

a 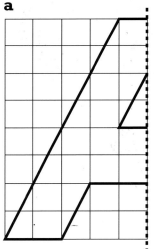 **b** 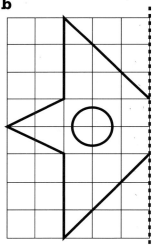 **c**

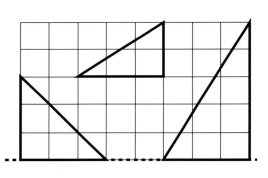

Draw the reflection of each shape so that the dotted line is a line of symmetry.

3 How many lines of symmetry do each of the following shapes have?

a  **b** 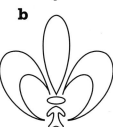 **c** **d** 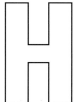 **e**

Reflections

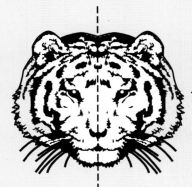

Put a mirror on the dotted line and look at the tiger from one side (it does not matter which).

You should see exactly the same in the mirror as you do without the mirror.

The dotted line is called an **axis** of symmetry.

One side of the picture is the **mirror image** of the other.

This axis of symmetry is **vertical**.

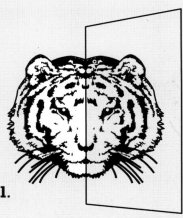

Here are some more axes of symmetry.

a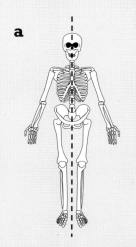

b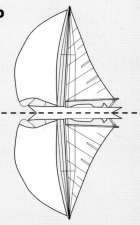

c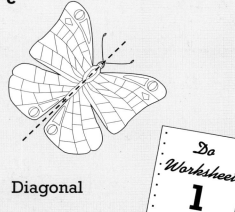

Diagonal

Vertical

Horizontal

Do Worksheet **1**

EXERCISE 1

Copy each diagram onto centimetre squared paper.
Complete it so that the dotted line is an axis of symmetry.

1 Vertical axis of symmetry

        a   **b**   **c**

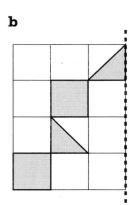
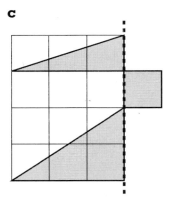

2 Horizontal axis of symmetry

   a   **b**   **c**

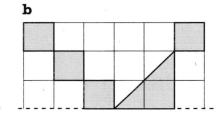
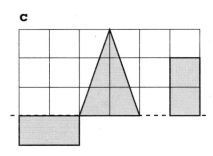

3 Diagonal axis of symmetry

   a   **b**   **c**

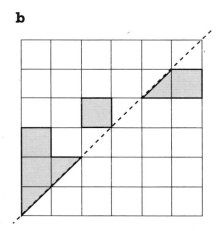
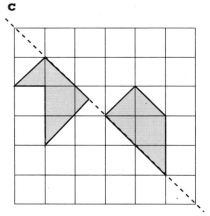

Do
Worksheet
2

Secret Codes

Andrew and Brian devised a
secret code using line symmetry.

For instance, the letter 'A' would look like this in code: A

And the letter 'B' would look like this: B

EXERCISE 2

Use a mirror to help you work out the messages Andrew and Brian sent to
each other.

1 HAVE YOU THE TIME

2 MEET ME AT THE ABBEY

3 CAN ETONY HOME ALIVE

4 THE BOOK MAY BE OUT

Do
Worksheet
3

We can use symmetry to work out missing sides and angles.

Example

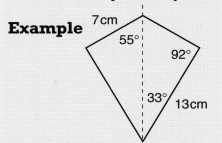

The dotted line is an axis of symmetry so …

$\longrightarrow$

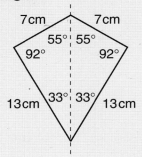

EXERCISE 3

The dotted lines are axes of symmetry.

1

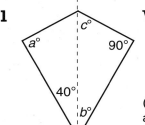

Work out the size of:
a a
b b
c c

(Remember: the angles of a triangle add up to 180°.)

2 Work out the size of:
a e
b f
c g

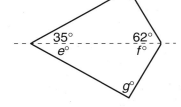

3

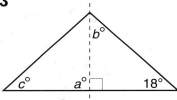

Find the value of:
a a
b b (Remember: the angles of a triangle ...)
c c

4 This shape has two axes of symmetry.

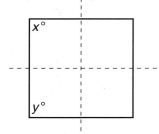

a What is the shape called?
b What is the size of: (i) x (ii) y?

5

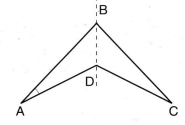

a Name a line equal to:
  (i) AB (ii) CD.

b Name an angle equal to:
  (i) ∠ABD (ii) ∠BCD.

6

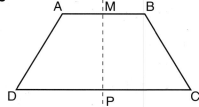

a Name a line equal to:
  (i) AM (ii) CP.

b Name an angle equal to:
  (i) ∠ADP (ii) ∠MBC.

7

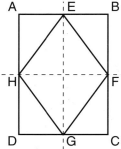

a Name two lines equal to:
  (i) EH (ii) BE.

b Name three angles equal to:
  (i) ∠AEH (ii) ∠HEG.

Glide Symmetry

Here is a pattern.
One part of it is
highlighted.

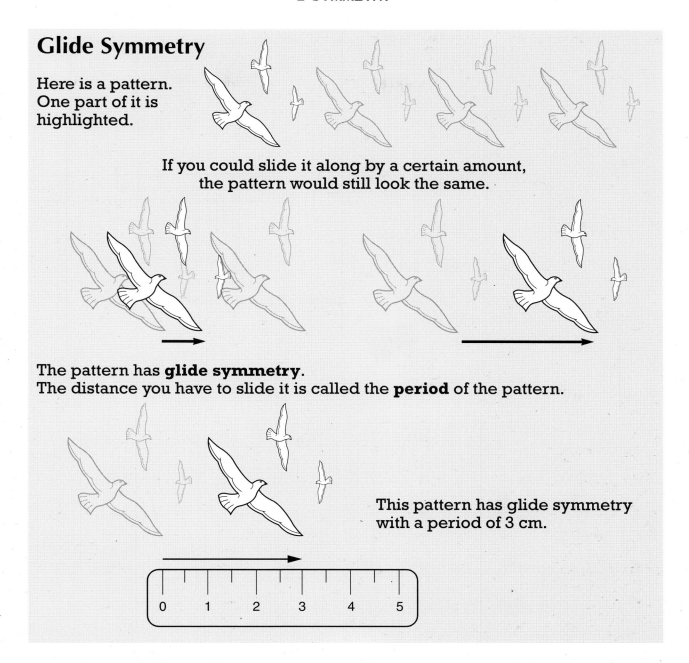

If you could slide it along by a certain amount,
the pattern would still look the same.

The pattern has **glide symmetry**.
The distance you have to slide it is called the **period** of the pattern.

This pattern has glide symmetry
with a period of 3 cm.

EXERCISE 4

1 Which of these patterns has glide symmetry?

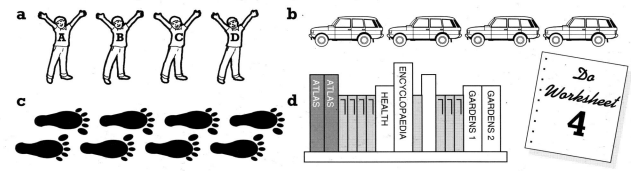

2 Measure the period of these patterns with a ruler.

a

b

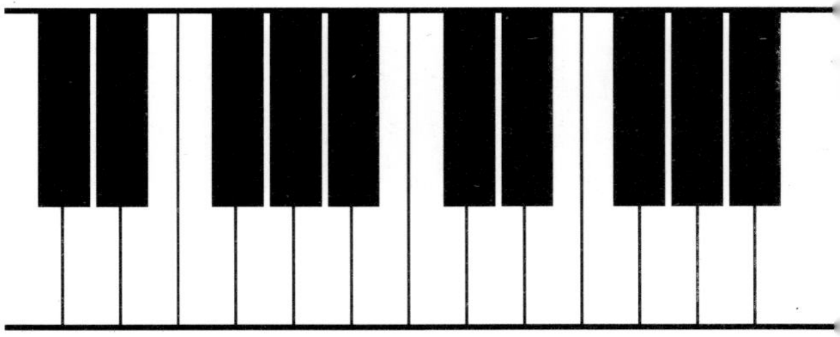

c

d

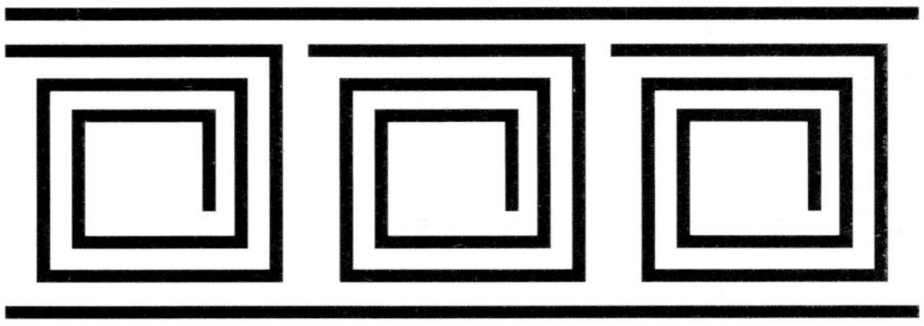

3 Archie the archaeologist studies a piece of tiling which he believes should have a period of **3 squares**. Can he rebuild the pattern?

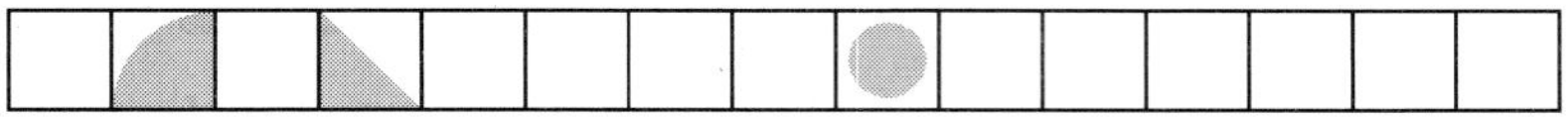

Step 1 Number the squares 1, 2, 3, 1, 2, 3, 1, 2, and so on.

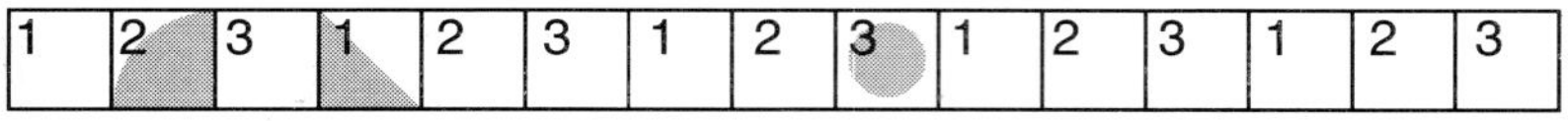

Step 2 All the squares marked '1' should have the same part of the pattern.

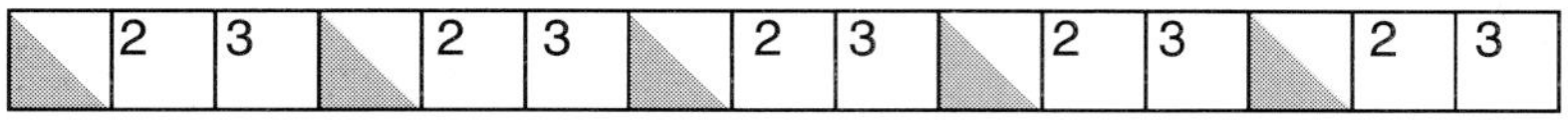

Step 3 This should also be true for all the tiles marked '2' and all tiles marked '3'.

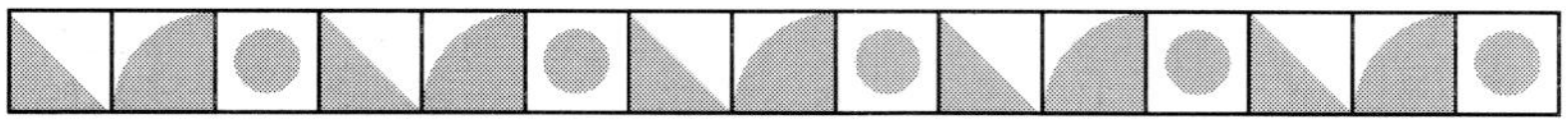

Copy and complete these tiles.

a Period 3 squares

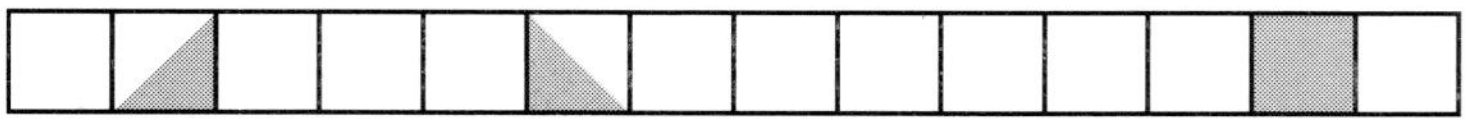

b Period 4 squares

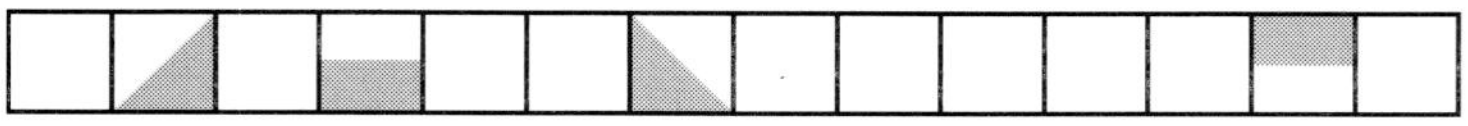

c Period 3 squares
(Do one row at a time.)

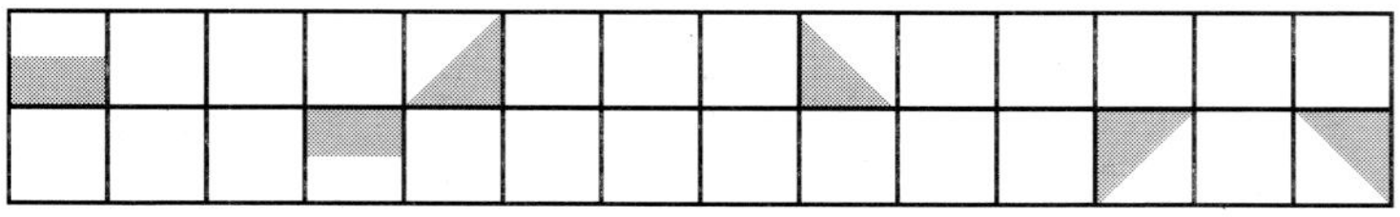

4 This diagram has glide symmetry. Copy it and fill in the sizes of as many angles as you can.

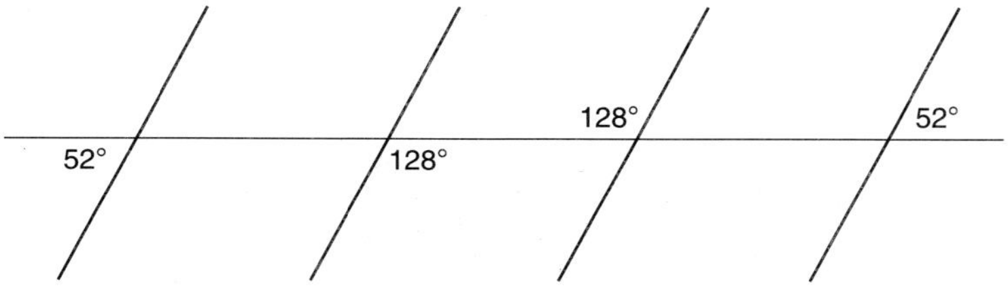

52°   128°   128°   52°

⭐ Rotation – Another Kind of Symmetry

Half-turn Symmetry

Turn the page upside-down and these pictures will still look the same.

You can make your own half-turn drawings.

Example

Trace this arrow.

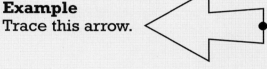

Lay the tracing exactly on top of the arrow

Put a pencil point on the solid dot

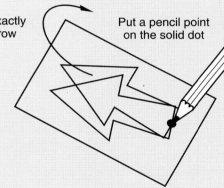

Give the tracing a half-turn

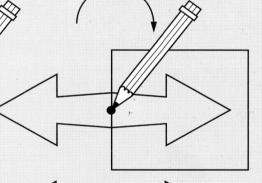

This new diagram has half-turn symmetry.
The dot is called the centre of symmetry.

EXERCISE 5

Copy each of the following diagrams.

Follow the steps above to give each diagram half-turn symmetry.

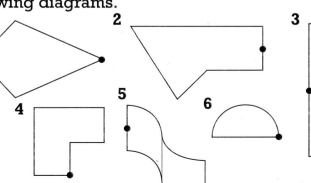

Further Turns

This looks the same twice when we give it a complete turn. It has turn symmetry of **order 2**.

This looks the same three times when we give it a complete turn.  It has turn symmetry of **order 3**.

If it looks the same four times, then it has **order 4** turn symmetry.

This has **order 5**. And this has **order 16**.

EXERCISE 6

1 Write down the order of turn symmetry for each of the following shapes.

a Wheel

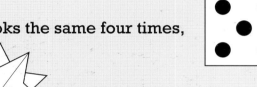

b Celtic design

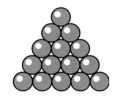

c Snooker balls

d Football

e Snowflake

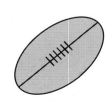

f Rugby ball

g Dartboard

2 Which faces of a dice show:

    a order 2 symmetry   **b** order 4 symmetry?

Drawings

You want to draw a pattern of order 3.

For a pattern to repeat three times in a complete turn (360°), it must appear every 360 ÷ 3 = 120°.

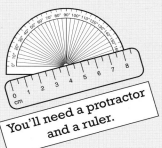

You'll need a protractor and a ruler.

1 Use your protractor to help you draw suitable guidelines.

2 Trace the pattern you want repeated (marking the centre).

3 Use the guidelines to help position the pattern. Keep the centre in the same spot each time.

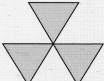

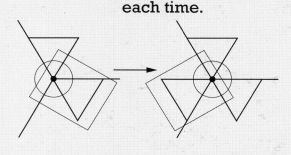

4 Rub out the guidelines.

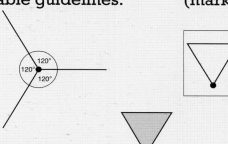

EXERCISE 6B

1 Use guidelines like those above to make pictures with order 3 symmetry out of the following:

a

b

c

(Careful! The centre is not on the shape.)

2 360° ÷ 4 = 90°.
Use guidelines similar to those opposite to make pictures with symmetry of order 4.

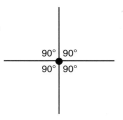

a

b

c

3 360° ÷ 5 = 72°.
  a Make suitable guidelines.
  b Make an order 5 symmetry picture using this: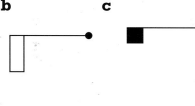
  c Make an order 6 symmetry picture.

CHECK-UP ON SYMMETRY

1 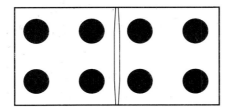 Copy this domino. Mark in all the axes of symmetry using dotted lines.

2 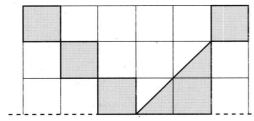 Copy and complete this diagram so that the dotted line is an axis of symmetry.

3 In this diagram the dotted line is an axis of symmetry.

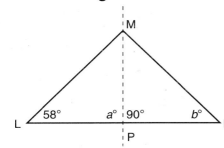

   a Name a line equal to NP.
   b Name a line equal to ML.
   c Find the value of: (i) $a°$ (ii) $b°$.

4 Copy this pattern onto squared paper. Continue the pattern across the page.

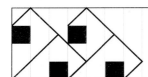

5 Copy this shape onto squared paper. Complete the diagram so that the shape has half-turn symmetry about the dot.

6 Write down the order of turn symmetry for this shape.

3 STRUCTURED DIAGRAMS

LOOKING BACK

1 Three friends were bird spotting.
The table shows how many birds
they saw.
Allan saw three blackbirds.

	Gull	Blackbird	Sparrow
Allan	2	3	5
Basani	4	1	2
Carol	3	2	4

a How many gulls did Basani see?
b How many birds did Carol see?
c How many sparrows did Allan see?
d How many sightings of sparrows were there?

2 A survey was done in the class
about coins. Everyone counted
their loose change.
A graph was made of the figures.
a How many 1p coins were in the class?
b How many 5p coins were in the class?
c How many silver coins were found?
d Which coin had the biggest count?

3 Find each output.

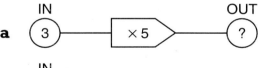

a

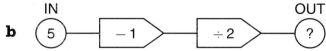

4 To hire a sunshade at the beach costs 50p deposit plus 50p an hour.

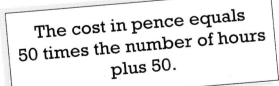

The cost in pence equals
50 times the number of hours
plus 50.

What is the cost
of hiring a
sunshade for:
a 1 hour
b 3 hours
c 6 hours?

5

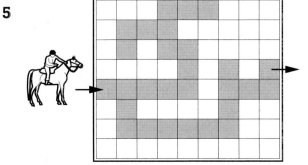

The horseman needs directions
through the maze.

These directions begin:
'Forward 2, turn right, forward 2, turn ...'

Continue the instructions.

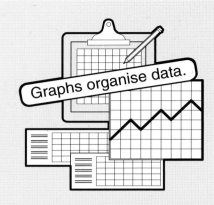

Graphs organise data.

Diagrams help us to organise our thoughts.

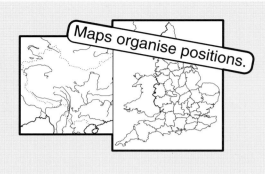

Maps organise positions.

Organising Possibilities: The Tree Diagram

Example Bill tosses a 10p and a 20p coin.
What could possibly happen?

This is called a **tree diagram** because of the way it branches.

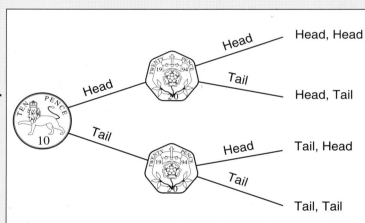

Head

Head ——— Head, Head

Tail ——— Head, Tail

Tail

Head ——— Tail, Head

Tail ——— Tail, Tail

The first branch shows that the 10p could fall heads or tails.

Each branch then branches to show that the 20p can also fall heads or tails.

The possibilities are then filled in by following each of the four trails.

EXERCISE 1

1 Would you like milk? Sugar?

Here is a tree diagram to show how these questions could be answered.

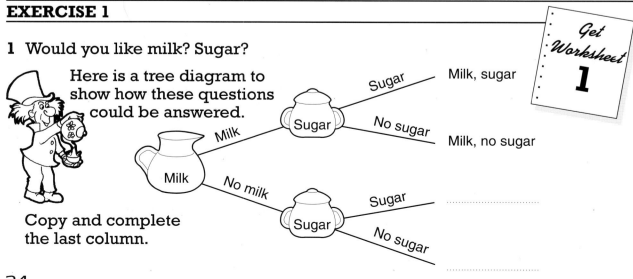

Milk

Sugar ——— Milk, sugar

No sugar ——— Milk, no sugar

No milk

Sugar ——— ....

No sugar ——— ....

Copy and complete the last column.

Get Worksheet **1**

2 Bryan could phone Kirsty. He could phone Laura.

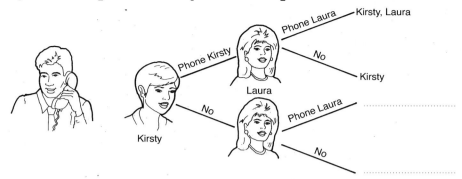

    a Copy and complete the tree diagram.
    b List the possible choices he has.

3 Jane has to pass three sets of traffic lights on the road to work. She may or may not get stopped at any one.

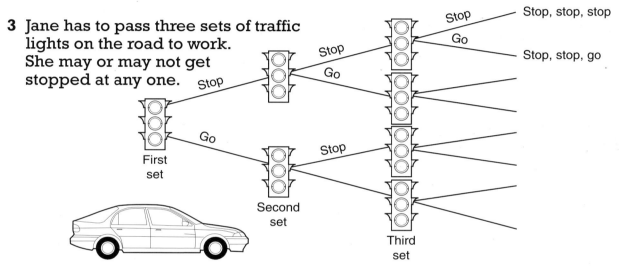

    a Copy and complete the tree diagram.
    b List the possible stoppage patterns Jane might get.

4 How many 2-digit numbers can you make using only the tiles shown?

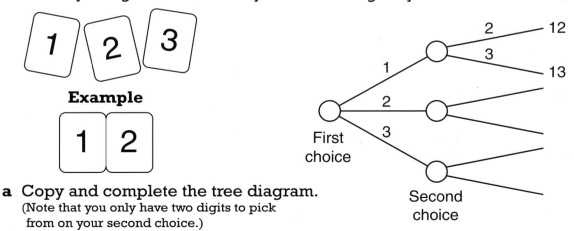

Example

    a Copy and complete the tree diagram.
    (Note that you only have two digits to pick from on your second choice.)
    b List all possible 2-digit numbers.
    c List all possible 3-digit numbers you can make using the numbers 1, 2 and 3.

5 How many dominoes can you make using only 1, 2 and 3?

  a Copy and complete the tree diagram.

  b The domino (2,1) will be the same as the domino (1,2). Score out duplicates and then list the possible dominoes.

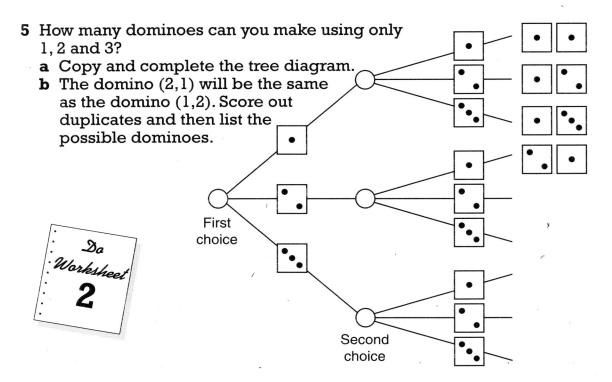

Do Worksheet 2

Organising Information: The Carroll Diagram

Lewis Carroll, the author of *Alice in Wonderland*, invented a type of diagram that helps with some problems. The diagram was named after him.

Example

Mairi took some coins from her bank. Some were round and some were not.

Some were silver and some were not.

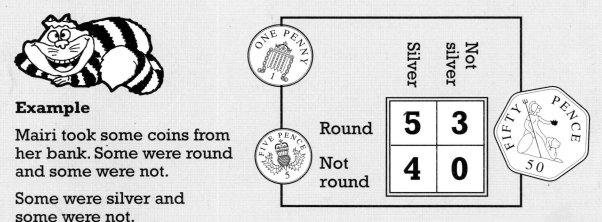

We can see from the Carroll diagram that:

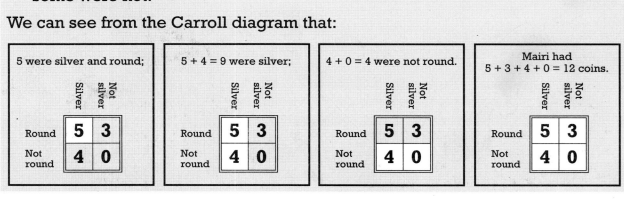

	Silver	Not silver
Round	5	3
Not round	4	0

5 were silver and round;

5 + 4 = 9 were silver;

4 + 0 = 4 were not round.

Mairi had 5 + 3 + 4 + 0 = 12 coins.

EXERCISE 2

1 Steve has some playing cards.
Some are face cards (and some
are not); some are red (and some
are not).

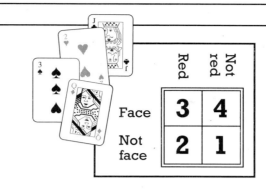

	Red	Not red
Face	3	4
Not face	2	1

  a How many are red face cards?
  b How many are not face cards?
  c How many are red cards?
  d How many cards has Steve?

2 On the bookshelf there were some
books. Some were hardbacks.
Some were maths books.
The Carroll diagram shows how
many of each type there were.

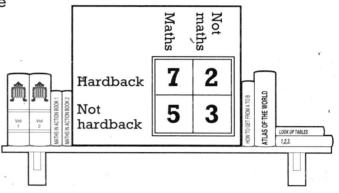

	Maths	Not maths
Hardback	7	2
Not hardback	5	3

  a How many maths books had
    hard covers?
  b How many maths books
    were there?
  c How many softbacked books
    were not maths books?
  d How many books were on
    the shelf?

3 There were several vehicles at the
builder's yard. Some were diggers.
Some were yellow.

	Yellow	Not yellow
Digger	5	0
Not digger	3	4

  a How many yellow vehicles were
    not diggers?
  b How many diggers were not yellow?
  c How many vehicles were in the yard?
  d How many yellow vehicles were there?

4 Some people ordered tea at a café.
Some took sugar, some took milk,
some took both and some took neither.

	Milk	Not milk
Sugar	3	7
Not sugar	5	6

  a How many took sugar but not milk?
  b How many took neither sugar nor milk?
  c How many took milk?
  d How many people ordered tea?

5 At an airshow some of the planes
were for passengers. Some were jets.

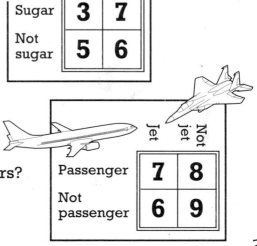

	Jet	Not jet
Passenger	7	8
Not passenger	6	9

  a How many passenger planes were jets?
  b How many planes were not for passengers?
  c How many planes were not jets?
  d How many planes were at the show?

6 In a survey people were asked these two questions:
'Do you believe in ghosts?'
'Do you believe in the Loch Ness Monster?'
  a How many believed in:
    (i) ghosts   (ii) the monster
    (iii) both   (iv) neither?
  b How many were asked?

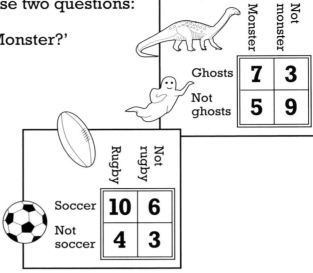

	Monster	Not monster
Ghosts	7	3
Not ghosts	5	9

7 Some people were asked if they
watched soccer or rugby.
  a How many watched:
    (i) soccer   (ii) rugby
    (iii) soccer but not rugby
    (iv) neither?
  b How many were asked?

	Rugby	Not rugby
Soccer	10	6
Not soccer	4	3

⭐ Making a Carroll Diagram

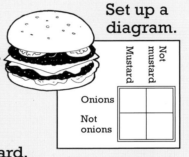

Set up a diagram.

	Mustard	Not mustard
Onions		
Not onions		

Example Read these statements.

1 The Quick Bite Bar sold 19
hamburgers at lunchtime.
2 Nine of them had onions.
3 Seven had mustard.
4 Four had both onions and mustard.

How many hamburgers had neither onions nor mustard?
Work through the statements backwards. Fill in the numbers in the diagram.

Four had both onions
and mustard.

	Mustard	Not mustard
Onions	4	
Not onions		

Seven had mustard.
We know four of these had
onions, so three had no onions.

	Mustard	Not mustard
Onions	4	
Not onions	3	

Nine had onions.
Four of these had mustard,
so five had no mustard.

	Mustard	Not mustard
Onions	4	5
Not onions	3	

19 hamburgers
were sold.

We know about
4 + 3 + 5 = 12,
so 7 had neither.

	Mustard	Not mustard
Onions	4	5
Not onions	3	7

Get Worksheet **3**

★ **EXERCISE 3**

1 16 friends went bird-spotting.
10 saw a thrush.
7 reported seeing a seagull.
6 reported seeing both.
  a How many only saw a seagull?
  b How many saw neither?

	Thrush	Not thrush
Gull	**6**	**1**
Not gull		

2 14 people were asked about their holidays.
9 had been to London.
3 had been abroad.
2 had done both.
How many had done neither?

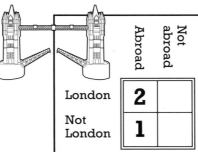

	Abroad	Not abroad
London	**2**	
Not London	**1**	

3 Henry conducted a survey about when his classmates went to bed.
He asked 17 pupils.
8 were boys.
11 said they went to bed after 10 pm.
7 boys said after 10 pm.
How many girls went to bed before 10 pm?

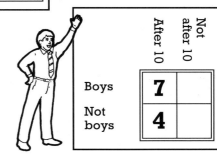

	After 10	Not after 10
Boys	**7**	
Not boys	**4**	

4 21 people were asked if they played golf and if they watched it on TV.
14 played the game.
9 watched golf on TV.
6 players watched it on TV.
How many of those asked did neither?

	Watched	Not watched
Played	**6**	
Not played	**3**	

5 Some people were questioned about their family.
7 said they had a brother.
9 said they had a sister.
4 said they had both.
What is the smallest number of people that could have been asked?

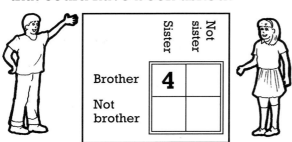

	Sister	Not sister
Brother	**4**	
Not brother		

Do Worksheet **4**

Organising Steps: The Flow Diagram

A flow diagram describes how a job should be done.

A title gives an idea of the job.

A rounded box is used to show where the job starts and stops.

A rectangular box holds the steps to be taken.

Arrows give an idea of the order in which to do the boxes.

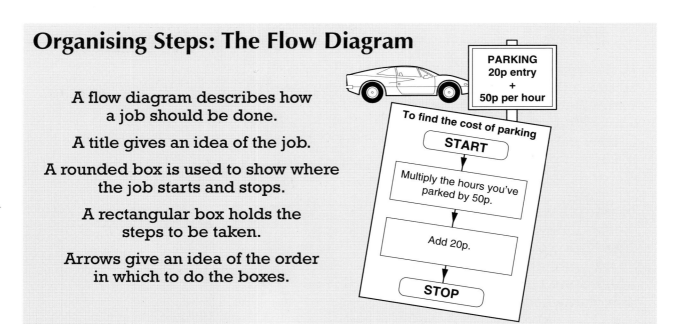

PARKING
20p entry
+
50p per hour

To find the cost of parking

START

Multiply the hours you've parked by 50p.

Add 20p.

STOP

EXERCISE 4

1 Use the flow diagram to help you share out:
   a 25 biscuits
   b 40 cups
   c 100 pencils
   amongst six people.

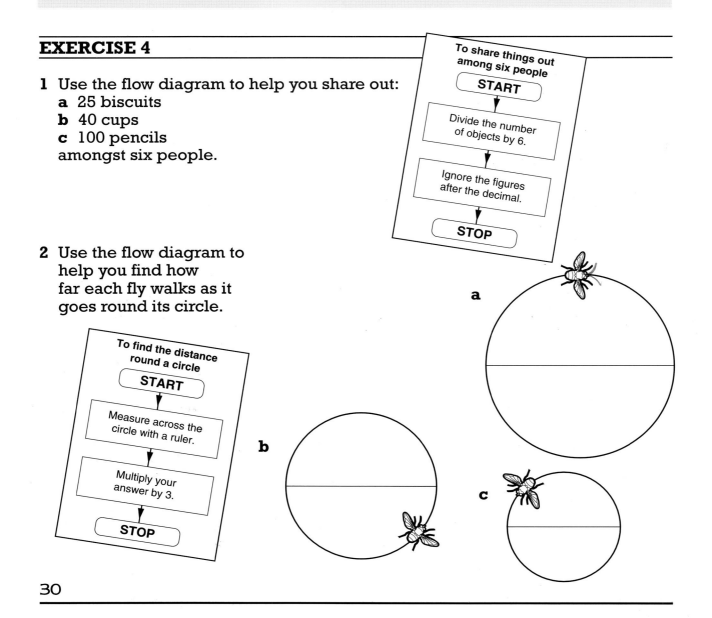

To share things out among six people

START

Divide the number of objects by 6.

Ignore the figures after the decimal.

STOP

2 Use the flow diagram to help you find how far each fly walks as it goes round its circle.

a

b

c

To find the distance round a circle

START

Measure across the circle with a ruler.

Multiply your answer by 3.

STOP

3

To find the average weight for a given age

START

Multiply age by 3.

Add 2.

STOP

This flowchart will help you work out the average weight in kilograms for someone of 10 years of age or less.

a What is the average weight for a 6-year-old?

b What is the average birth weight? (Age = 0 years)

c Jack is 10 years old and weighs 33 kg. Is he above or below average?

4 When you buy many things you have to pay a tax called value added tax (VAT). Use this flow diagram to help you work out how much tax you pay on these items.

a

c

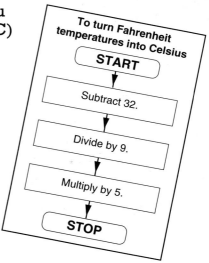

£8

£2

b

£12

To work out VAT

START

Multiply the price by 17.5.

Divide by 100.

STOP

5

To turn Celsius temperatures into Fahrenheit

START

Divide by 5.

Multiply by 9.

Add 32.

STOP

These two charts help you swop between Celsius (°C) and Fahrenheit (°F) temperatures.

a Change these to °F:
(i)   30 °C   (ii) 45 °C
(iii) 100 °C

b Change these to °C:
(i)   50 °F   (ii) 41 °F
(iii) 122 °F

To turn Fahrenheit temperatures into Celsius

START

Subtract 32.

Divide by 9.

Multiply by 5.

STOP

6 Sometimes you have a choice of ways to go.
A diamond-shaped box holds a question.
You will know which route to go when you
answer the question.

Cycle hire

Adults £3 per hour
Children £2 per hour

How much does a cycle cost:

a an adult for 2 hours
b an adult for 5 hours
c a child for 4 hours?

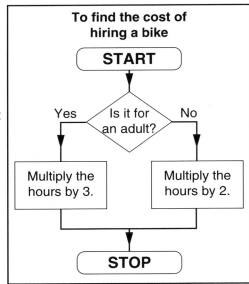

To find the cost of hiring a bike

START

Is it for an adult?

Yes → Multiply the hours by 3.

No → Multiply the hours by 2.

STOP

7

Cooking times

START

Is it chicken?

Yes → Multiply the weight by 40 minutes.

No → Multiply the weight by 30 minutes.

Add an extra 40 minutes.

STOP

This flow diagram helps you work out
the cooking times for chicken or beef.

How long do you need to cook:
a a 2 kg chicken
b a 3 kg piece of beef?

8 The Hotel Splendide charges more for
the summer months of June, July and August.
They also have to charge you tax.

The flow diagram will help you
work out the bill for:

a 10 days in March
b 7 days in July
c 14 days in June.

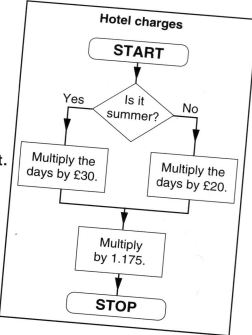

Hotel charges

START

Is it summer?

Yes → Multiply the days by £30.

No → Multiply the days by £20.

Multiply by 1.175.

STOP

CHECK-UP ON STRUCTURED DIAGRAMS

1 A cartoonist has these choices when he draws a face:

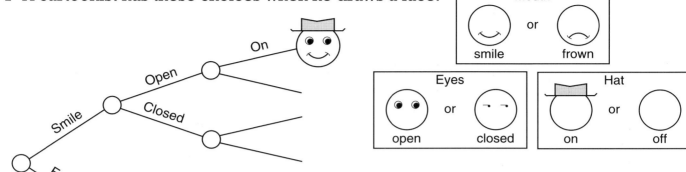

Copy and complete the tree diagram to help you find all the possible cartoon faces.

2 Some people were asked if they had been stung by a wasp or bitten by midges.

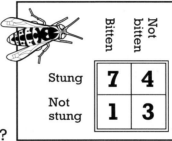

	Bitten	Not bitten
Stung	7	4
Not stung	1	3

a How many had been stung?
b How many had been bitten?
c How many had been bitten but not stung?

3

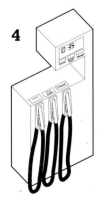

	Toys	Not toys
Men		
Not men		

20 adults were asked if they still had some of their childhood toys.

12 said they did have some of their toys.
11 men were asked.
5 men said they still had some toys.

Copy and complete the Carroll diagram. How many women had not kept any toys?

4 The cost of petrol depends on whether it is unleaded or not. Use the flow diagram to find the cost of:

a 20 litres unleaded
b 45 litres leaded
c 10 litres
   (i) leaded
   (ii) unleaded.

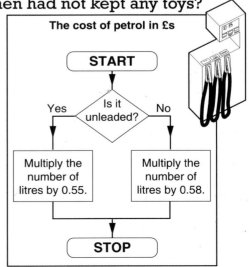

The cost of petrol in £s

START

Is it unleaded?
Yes — No

Multiply the number of litres by 0.55.

Multiply the number of litres by 0.58.

STOP

4 A PROBLEM SOLVING TOOLKIT

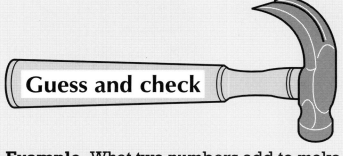

Guess and check

You've got a problem.

1 Guess the answer.

2 Test your guess.

3 Improve your guess.

Example What two numbers add to make 8 and subtract to make 2?

Guess: 0 and 8
Test: $0 + 8 = 8$ but $8 - 0 \neq 2$
Guess: 1 and 7
Test: $1 + 7 = 8$ but $7 - 1 \neq 2$
Guess: 2 and 6
Test: $2 + 6 = 8$ but $6 - 2 \neq 2$
Guess: 3 and 5
Test: $3 + 5 = 8$ and $5 - 3 = 2$

3 and 5 fit the description.

This is also known as
trial and error
and
trial and improvement.

EXERCISE 1

1 Find two numbers which add to make 10 and subtract to make 4.

2 Find two numbers which multiply to make 12 and subtract to make 1.

3 Find two numbers which multiply to make 36 and add to make 13.

4 Find two numbers which add to make 17 and whose difference is 5.

5

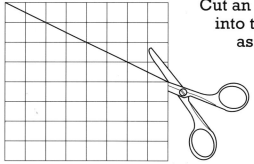

Cut an 8×8 square
into two pieces
as shown.

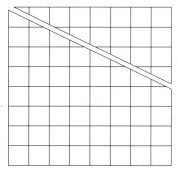

Use the two pieces to make:
a a right-angled triangle **b** a parallelogram **c** a trapezium **d** a pentagon.
Glue your answers into your jotter.

6 Use sticks to form this pattern of 5 squares.
Take away 3 sticks to leave 3 squares.

Record your answer by drawing a diagram.

Get Worksheet **1**

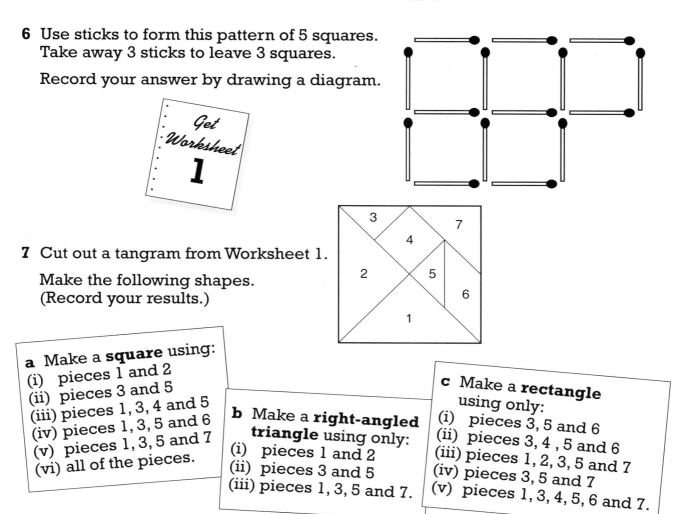

7 Cut out a tangram from Worksheet 1.

Make the following shapes.
(Record your results.)

a Make a **square** using:
(i)   pieces 1 and 2
(ii) pieces 3 and 5
(iii) pieces 1, 3, 4 and 5
(iv) pieces 1, 3, 5 and 6
(v) pieces 1, 3, 5 and 7
(vi) all of the pieces.

b Make a **right-angled triangle** using only:
(i)   pieces 1 and 2
(ii) pieces 3 and 5
(iii) pieces 1, 3, 5 and 7.

c Make a **rectangle** using only:
(i)   pieces 3, 5 and 6
(ii) pieces 3, 4 , 5 and 6
(iii) pieces 1, 2, 3, 5 and 7
(iv) pieces 3, 5 and 7
(v) pieces 1, 3, 4, 5, 6 and 7.

8 Use all the pieces of your tangram to make each of these shapes.

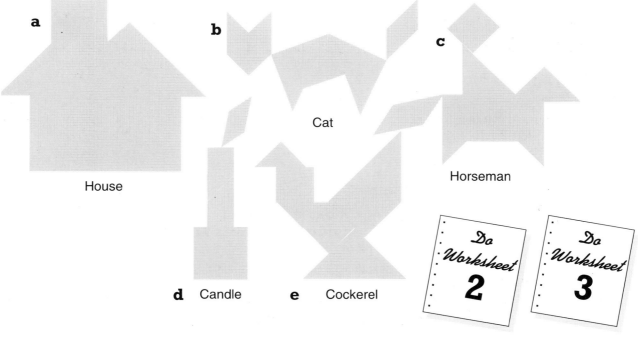

a House

b Cat

c Horseman

d Candle   **e** Cockerel

Do Worksheet **2**   *Do Worksheet* **3**

Use a Model

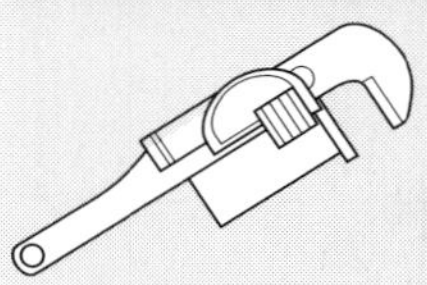

Often a puzzle or a problem is best solved
by making a model and acting it out.

Example We have four frogs sitting on five lilypads.

A frog can leap to the next pad.

A frog can leap over another frog to the next pad.

A frog cannot leap backwards.

Can you get the frogs into this position?

Make the models and try the problem.

Get Worksheet **4**

EXERCISE 2

1 Make figure 1 look like figure 2.

Rules
Pieces can slide horizontally,
vertically or diagonally
into empty spaces.

fig. 1

fig. 2

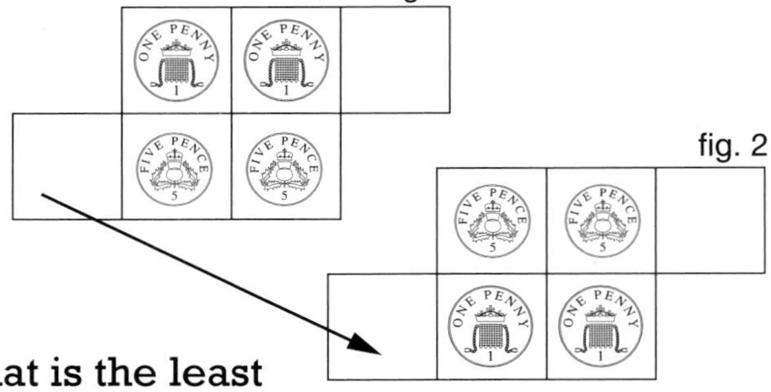

What is the least
number of moves needed?

2 Try the frog problem with six frogs and seven lilypads.

3 Slide the tile marked X
onto the square marked Y.

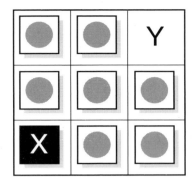

Blocks can be slid horizontally
or vertically into an empty square.

What is the smallest number of
moves needed?

4

To practise their compass bearings
five pupils stepped away from a pole
on different routes.

Meg: 2 East, 3 North, 2 East, 3 North.
      (Her route is shown.)
Kim: 4 East, 2 North, 2 East, 1 North.
Lee: 2 North, 2 West, 3 North, 2 West.
Will: 4 West, 1 North, 2 East, 2 South.
Fred: 2 South, 4 East, 1 North, 3 West.

Use centimetre squared paper.
Draw all five routes.
Use a ruler to list the pupils in order of
their distance from the pole.
Start with whoever is furthest from the pole.

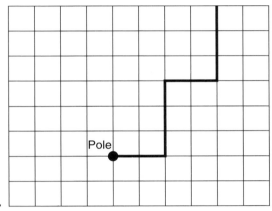

5 How many of these circles can Ken cut
from an A4 sheet of paper?

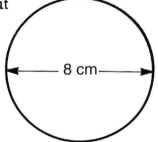
←——— 8 cm ———→

6 Najma uses six plastic squares
to make this shape.

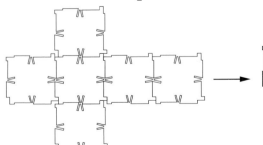

It folds up into a cube.
It is the **net** of a cube.

There are only eleven different nets.
Here is another one.
Can you find all the rest?

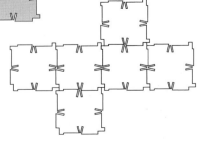

Do
Worksheet
5

Make a Table or an Organised List

Example

Mike, Alan and some friends went out for a meal.
They each chose three things from the menu
opposite: a starter, a main course and a sweet.

Quick Bite

Starters:	Soup Melon
Main course:	Chicken Beef
Sweet:	Fruit Gateau

Mike chose soup, chicken and fruit (SCF).
Alan chose soup, chicken and gateau (SCG).
In fact they all chose a different combination.

How many different combinations are possible?

Make a list. Be organised so as not to miss or repeat any options.

(SCF), (SCG), (SBF), (SBG), (MCF), (MCG), (MBF), (MBG)

There are eight possible choices.

EXERCISE 3

1 How many different 3-digit numbers can you make using the numbers below?

Make an **organised list** by writing the
numbers in order from smallest to largest.
(A tree diagram might help.)

2 The combination of a safe is made up of four different numbers.
Jo knows that the four numbers are:

How many different combinations are possible?
Remember to make an **organised list**.

3 How many triangles are in this diagram?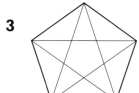

Hint: label all the points.

Ask yourself: 'How many triangles have AB for a side?'

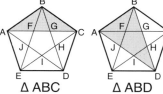   Δ ABC

   Δ ABD

   Δ ABE

   Δ ABF

   Δ ABG

   Δ ABJ

Ask yourself: 'How many triangles have AC for a side?'

4 Four friends, Frank, Ellie, Ito and Sally each have a pet.
Copy the table.

Use the clues to complete the table.
The table will help you to organise
the information.

Name	Pet	Pet's name

Clues
Frank's pet is a goldfish.
Ellie's pet is called Bronx.
The snake is called Rambo.
The cat is called Killer.
Sally does not own the snake.
The dog is not called Fang.

5 The prizewinners at the Hallowe'en Ball
were Adam, Bakula, Colin and Dave.
Copy the table.

Use the clues to complete the table.
The table will help you to organise
the information.

Name	Costume	Prize

Clues
Bakula won first prize.
The monster came in second.
The skeleton was fourth.
Adam dressed as the mummy.
Dave was not the monster.
The witch did not get third prize.

6 Three teams set up a basketball mini-
league and played the games shown.

Alder never beat Baxter.
The Crown never lost a home game.
The Crown lost two games.
There were no draws.

a Use the clues to help you fill in the table below.

Game	Home team		Away team
1	Alder	v	Crown
2	Crown	v	Alder
3	Baxter	v	Alder
4	Alder	v	Baxter
5	Baxter	v	Crown
6	Crown	v	Baxter

Away team

Home team

	A	B	C
A			
B			
C			

c Who won the tournament?

b A team gets two points for a win,
one for a draw and nothing for losing.
Copy and complete this table.

Name	Won	Drawn	Lost	Points
Alder				
Baxter				
Crown				

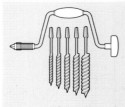

Look for a Pattern

Making an organised list or table often helps you to
spot a pattern.
Look at the **steps** between terms.

Example 1 What is the tenth term in this list of numbers?
2, 4, 6, 8, 10, ...
Notice they go up in steps of 2. We have the **two times table**.
Check it!
So $2 \times 10 = 20$.
20 is the tenth number on the list.

Example 2 What is the tenth term in this list of numbers?
1, 3, 5, 7, 9, ...
Notice they go up in steps of 2. We have the **two times table**
again. But check it! We have to **take away 1** from each number.
So $2 \times 10 = 20$, then $20 - 1 = 19$.
19 is the tenth number on the list.

EXERCISE 4

1

1, 3, 5, 7, 9 ... is the two
times table with 1
subtracted from each term.
The tenth number in the list
is 19.

In a similar way, for each of the lists below:
(i)   say which times table is involved
(ii) say what has been done to each term
(iii) work out the tenth number in the list.

a 3, 5, 7, 9, ...   **b** 6, 10, 14, 18, ...   **c** 1, 4, 7, 10, ...   **d** 5, 11, 17, 23, ...
e 2, 7, 12, 17, ...   **f** 16, 18, 20, 22, ...   **g** 5, 8, 11, 14, ...   **h** 9, 19, 29, 39, ...

2  Jan is doing some matchstick puzzles. For each set of diagrams work
out how many matchsticks she will need for the twentieth diagram.

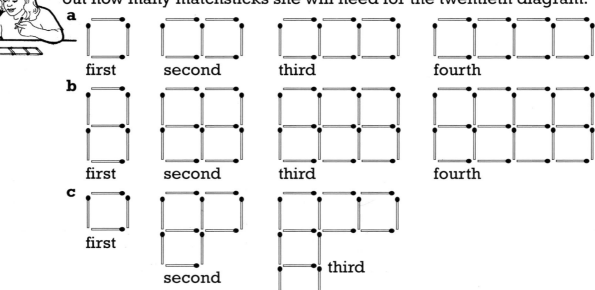

a
first   second   third   fourth

b
first   second   third   fourth

c
first
second
third

3 Maria has a charm bracelet. Each link can clip to four things (either trinkets or other links).

1 link
4 trinkets

2 links
6 trinkets

3 links
8 trinkets

a How many trinkets will you get on four links?
b Describe the pattern which is building up. (4, 6, 8, …)
c How many will you get with 20 links?

Do Worksheet **7**

 **Try a Simpler Case**

Example

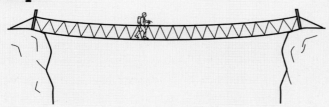

Across Terror Gulch hangs a rope bridge 200 metres long.
A rope zig-zags between a hand rail and a foot rail.
It is knotted at each turn.
The knots are 1 m apart.
How many knots are in the bridge?

Look at a 1 metre bridge.   Look at a 2 metre bridge.   Look at a 3 metre bridge.

 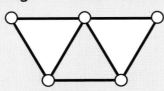 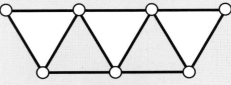

3 knots   5 knots   7 knots

It is **1 more** than the **two times table**.
$$200 \times 2 = 400$$
$$400 + 1 = 401$$
There are 401 knots.

EXERCISE 5

1 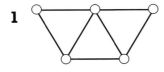   Here is a 2 m section of the Terror Gulch Bridge.
You can see that it has seven rope sections.
How many rope sections are in the whole bridge?

2 An exhibition hall has a square floor measuring 50 m by 50 m.

The floor is covered with carpet tiles.
Each tile is 1 m by 1 m.

A diagonal line is drawn from one corner
to the other.
How many tiles are affected?

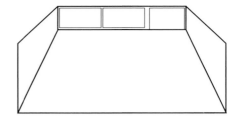

Try some simpler cases.

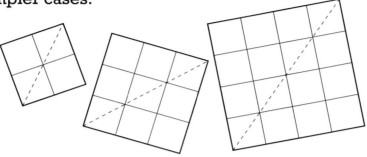

3 a Another area of the hall is a rectangular floor measuring 100 m by 60 m.
Again a line is drawn diagonally from corner to corner.
How many tiles are affected?

Here is a simpler case to try.
Notice it is 10 m by 6 m.
(We could also have used 5 by 3.)

b How many tiles would be
affected in a 36 m by 24 m area?

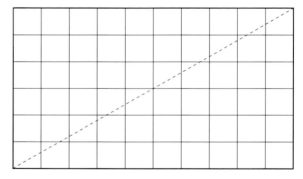

4 Arrange seven 2p and seven 20p coins as shown.

You can switch the positions of any pair of neighbouring coins.
This counts as a move.

How many moves will it take to get the coins like this?

Try some simpler cases.

5 Add up all the numbers from 1 to 100.

Try some simpler cases. Add the numbers from 1 to 10.
Here is a trick.

We want this: $1 + 2 + 3 + 4 + 5 + 6 + 7 + 8 + 9 + 10$

or this: $10 + 9 + 8 + 7 + 6 + 5 + 4 + 3 + 2 + 1$

Add them: $11 + 11 + 11 + 11 + 11 + 11 + 11 + 11 + 11 + 11 = 110$

Which is twice what we want. So we want $110 \div 2 = 55$.

6 Add up all the numbers from 1 to 1000.

CHECK-UP ON PROBLEM SOLVING

1 Six people met at a party.
They all shook hands with each other.
How many handshakes happened?

2 A man has a cabbage, a rabbit
and a pet tiger which he wishes
to ferry across a river.
His boat is so small that he can
only transport one of these things
at a time.
But he can't leave the tiger and
the rabbit alone, and he can't leave
the rabbit with the cabbage.
How does he get all three across safely?

Use a model.

3

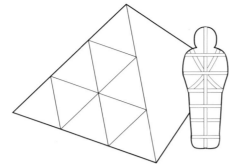

How many triangles are on the front of the mummy's tomb?

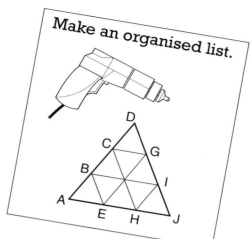

Make an organised list.

4 Adam, Bakula, Chris and Diane went on holiday.
They each travelled differently: by car, bus, plane and train.
They each went to different places: Rome, Paris, Madrid and London.

Use the clues below to find out:
a where Bakula went
b how Chris got to his destination.

Make a table.

Adam went to Rome.
Bakula took the train.
The car went to London.
The bus did not go to Rome or Paris.
Diane didn't take the bus.

Person	Transport	Place

5 Here are three patterns.
(i) Describe each. (ii) Find the tenth term.

a 2, 7, 12, 17 … **b** 23, 30, 37, 44 … **c** 9, 15, 21, 27 …

Look for a pattern

Try a simpler case

6

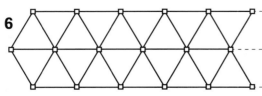

A bridge is 100 m long.
Its side is built from girders and bolts. Here is a 1 m section.
How many:
a girders **b** bolts
are needed for the 100 m side?

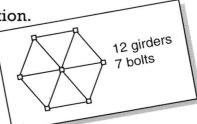

12 girders
7 bolts

5 SCALES

LOOKING BACK

1 Sam, Jon and Alan played a dice game.
Their final scores are shown on the scoreboard below.

   a Write down the name of each player and his score.
   b If Jon was the winner of the game, who was last?

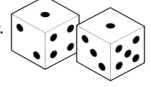

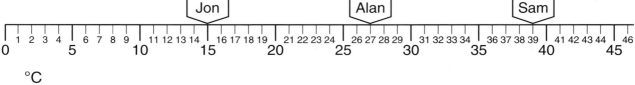

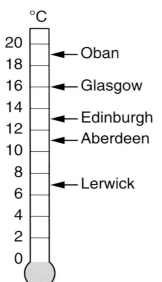

2 These temperatures were recorded in a few towns around Scotland one Friday in May. The temperatures were recorded in degrees Celsius (°C).

It was 13 °C in Edinburgh.

   a Make a list of the other places.
   b Write down the temperature recorded in each place beside its name.

3 The pine tree is 39 feet tall.

Write down the names
and the heights of
the other trees.

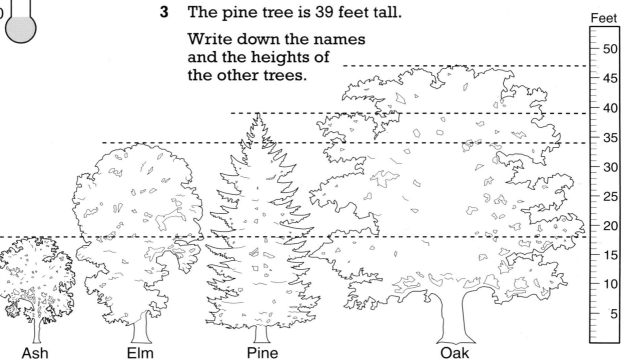

Ash   Elm   Pine   Oak

Some scales do not show all the numbers.
You must work out what number goes next to each mark
on the scale.

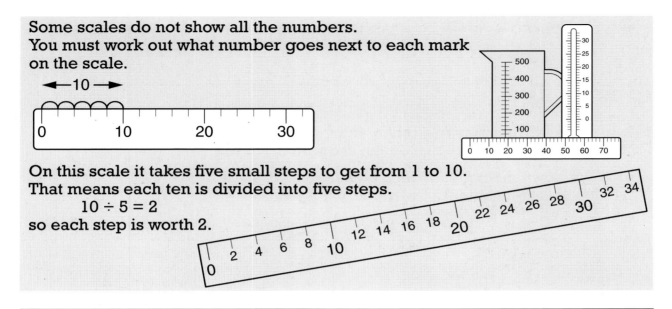

On this scale it takes five small steps to get from 1 to 10.
That means each ten is divided into five steps.

$10 \div 5 = 2$

so each step is worth 2.

EXERCISE 1

1 The Jones children are saving for their holiday.
The scale below shows how much each child has saved.

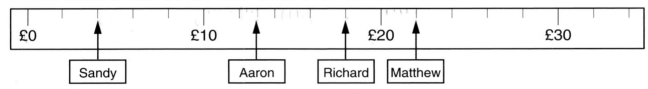

Write down each child's name and how much they have saved.

2 Four weeks later the children record how much they have now saved.

a Write down how much each has now.

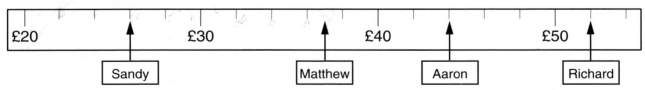

b Whose savings went up by the greatest amount during the four weeks?
(Remember to show all your working.)

3 By the time their holiday arrived they had saved the following amounts.

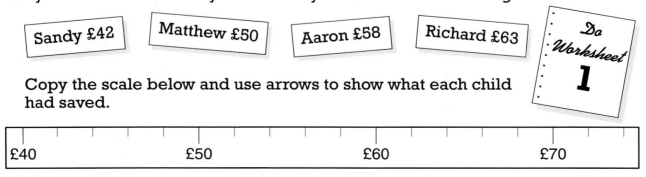

Sandy £42   Matthew £50   Aaron £58   Richard £63

Do
Worksheet
1

Copy the scale below and use arrows to show what each child
had saved.

On each of these scales we see the same numbers.

Each scale is different.

The marks in between stand for different numbers.

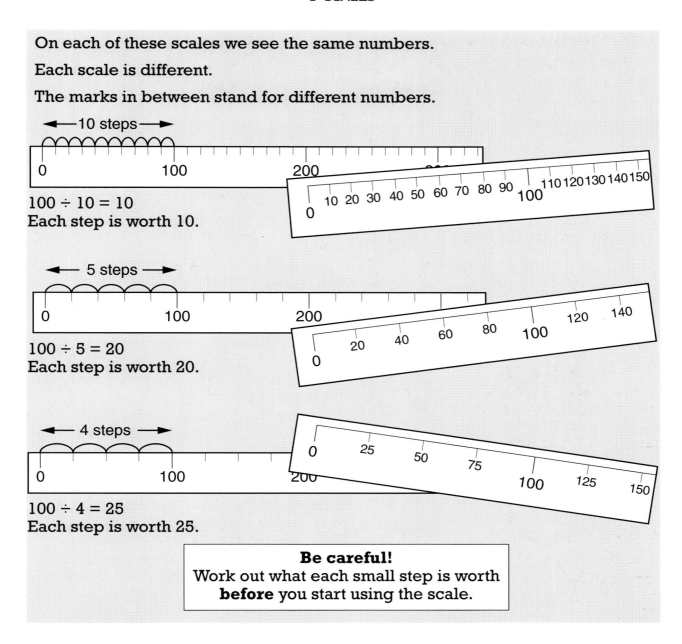

$100 \div 10 = 10$
Each step is worth 10.

$100 \div 5 = 20$
Each step is worth 20.

$100 \div 4 = 25$
Each step is worth 25.

Be careful!
Work out what each small step is worth
before you start using the scale.

EXERCISE 2

1 Jo and her friends collect pop stickers.
The number of stickers each girl has is shown on the scale below.

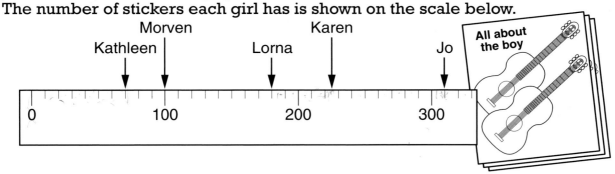

Write down the name of each girl and how many stickers she has.

2 The distances from Carlisle to other UK towns and cities are shown below.

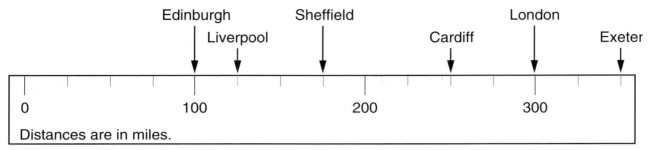

Distances are in miles.

How far is it from Carlisle to:

a London **b** Edinburgh **c** Cardiff **d** Liverpool **e** Sheffield **f** Exeter?

3

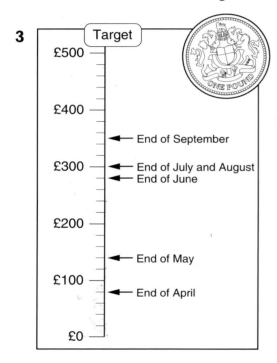

Class 4T2 collects pound coins for charity. At the end of each month they show the amount collected, so far, on a class wall chart.

a How much money was collected by the end of April?

b How much money was collected altogether by the end of May?

c How much was collected *during* May?

d How much was collected by the end of September?

e How much more do they need to reach their target?

f The main fund-raising event was a charity disco. In which month do you think it was held? Give a reason for your answer.

g Why do you think very little was collected between the end of June and the end of August?

4

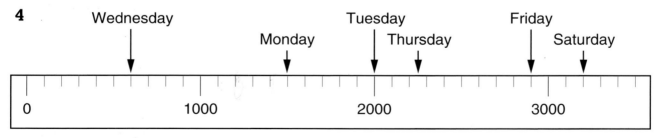

The number of people attending a fun fair each day is shown above.

a How many people does each small step on the scale stand for?

b How many people attended the fun fair on Monday?

c One day the weather was cold and wet. Explain which day you think it was.

d Copy and complete the table.

Mon	Tue	Wed	Thu	Fri	Sat
				2900	

Measures

The ruler measures lengths in centimetres.

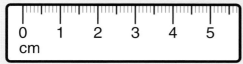

Each centimetre is divided into 10 parts.
1 cm ÷ 10 = 0.1 cm.
Each small division on the ruler is worth 0.1 cm.

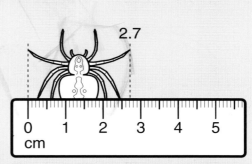

This spider measures 2.7 cm.

EXERCISE 3

1 Write down the name and width of each of these flowers.

a Common daisy

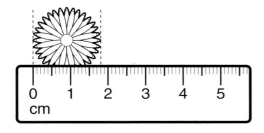

b Buttercup

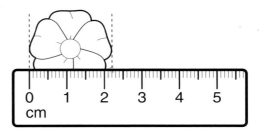

c Pansy

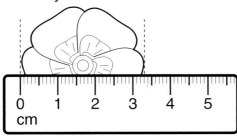

d Thistle

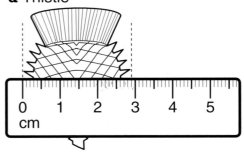

2

This jug contains **1.3 litres** of juice.

Write down how many litres of juice are in each of these jugs.

a   **b**   **c**

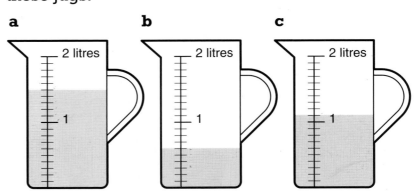

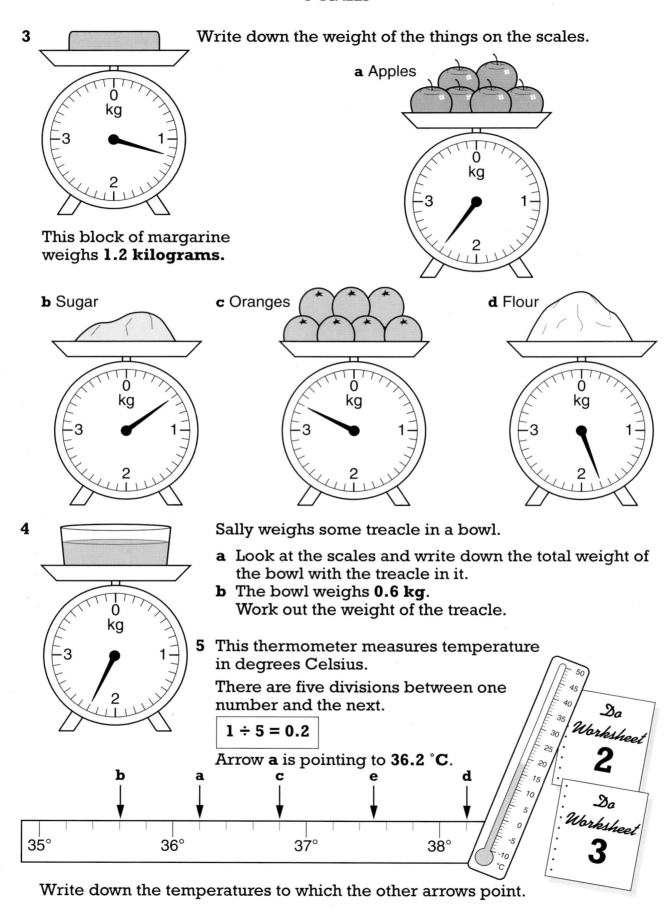

3 Write down the weight of the things on the scales.

a Apples

This block of margarine weighs **1.2 kilograms.**

b Sugar   **c** Oranges   **d** Flour

4 Sally weighs some treacle in a bowl.

a Look at the scales and write down the total weight of the bowl with the treacle in it.

b The bowl weighs **0.6 kg**.
Work out the weight of the treacle.

5 This thermometer measures temperature in degrees Celsius.

There are five divisions between one number and the next.

$1 \div 5 = 0.2$

Arrow **a** is pointing to **36.2 °C**.

Do Worksheet **2**

Do Worksheet **3**

Write down the temperatures to which the other arrows point.

CALDERVALE HIGH SCHOOL
TOWERS ROAD
AIRDRIE
ML6 8PG

More Accurate Measures

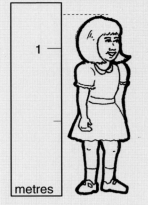

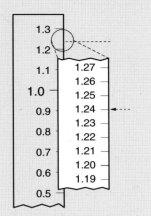

From a distance we can see that Sian is about 1 metre tall.

To be more accurate we need to look closer. Sian is just over 1.2 metres tall.

If we look even closer, we see that Sian is 1.24 metres tall.

EXERCISE 4

1 Write down the number to which each arrow points. Remember that 1.5 is the same as 1.50.

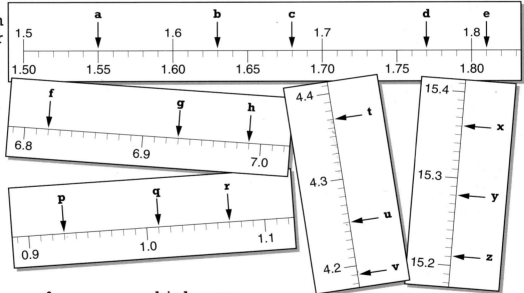

2 The wingspans of some young birds were measured in metres.

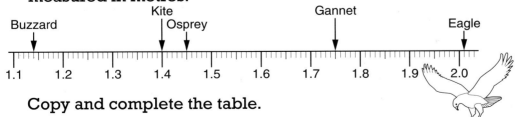

Copy and complete the table.

Bird	Buzzard	Kite	Osprey	Gannet	Eagle
Wingspan (metres)					

Do Worksheet **4**

Temperature

A thermometer measures temperature.
The scales on thermometers are often
different.

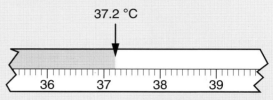

| Water freezes at | 0 °C | ❄ | 32 °F |
| Water boils | at 100 °C | 🫖 | 212 °F |

This thermometer has
every degree marked.

13 °C

This one has every
2 degrees marked.

24 °C

We need to be more accurate
when taking a person's
temperature.

37.2 °C

36   37   38   39

This thermometer has every 0.1°
marked.

EXERCISE 5

1 Write down the
temperatures
in these cities
around the world.

a This thermometer
measures in °C.

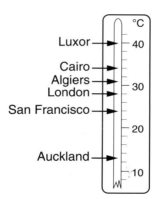

°C
Luxor — 40
Cairo —
Algiers —   30
London —
San Francisco —
20
Auckland —
10

b This thermometer
measures in °F.

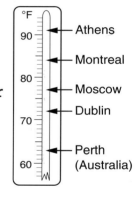

°F
90 — Athens
— Montreal
80
— Moscow
— Dublin
70
60 — Perth
(Australia)

2 A nurse took
the temperature
of four patients
in hospital.
Write down
each patient's
name and
temperature.

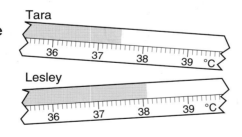

Tara
36   37   38   39   °C

Jim
36   37   38   39   °C

Lesley
36   37   38   39   °C

Laura
36   37   38   39   °C

3 There are three
ovens in the
cookery room.
What
temperature
is shown
on each
dial?

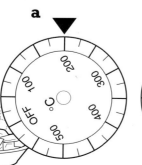

a

200
100   300
OFF   400
500   °C

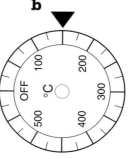

b

100
OFF   200
°C   300
500   400

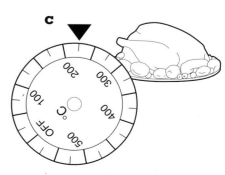

c

200
100   300
OFF   400
500   °C

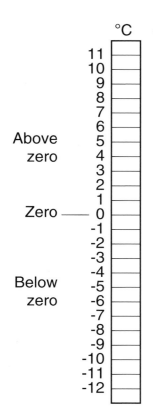

°C

Above zero

Zero

Below zero

Temperatures Below Zero

On a cold day the temperature can drop below zero.

Two degrees **below** zero is called **negative 2 °C** (or minus 2 °C).

We write – **2 °C**.

If the temperature is four degrees **above** zero we write 4 °C.

EXERCISE 6

1 How would we write:

   a five degrees below zero
   b one degree below zero
   c seven degrees above zero
   d three degrees below freezing?

2 Write down the temperatures shown on these thermometers.

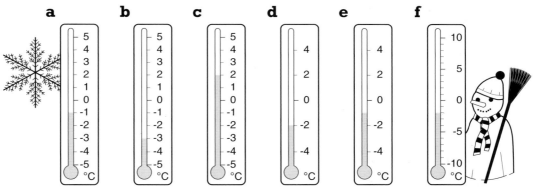

  a   **b**   **c**   **d**   **e**   **f**

3 One January day the temperature was recorded around Scotland.
The results are shown on the scale below.

JANUARY

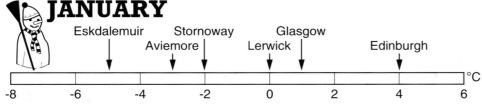

   a Which places had temperatures below zero?
   b What was the temperature in Aviemore?
   c What was the temperature in Edinburgh?
   d Which place was warmer, Stornoway or Glasgow?
   e How many degrees warmer was Lerwick than Eskdalemuir?

More Scales Using Negative Numbers

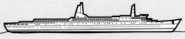

Negative numbers can be used to
stand for depth below sea-level.
5 metres means 5 metres above sea-level.
0 metres stands for sea-level.
–6 metres means 6 metres below sea-level.

EXERCISE 7

1

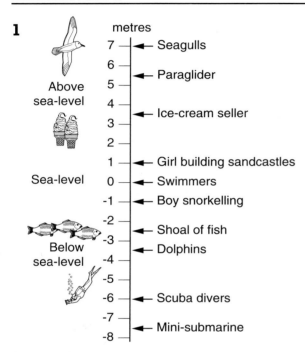

metres

7 ← Seagulls
6
← Paraglider
5
4
← Ice-cream seller
3
2
1 ← Girl building sandcastles
0 ← Swimmers
-1 ← Boy snorkelling
-2
← Shoal of fish
-3
← Dolphins
-4
-5
-6 ← Scuba divers
-7
← Mini-submarine
-8

Above sea-level

Sea-level

Below sea-level

a How high are the seagulls flying?
b At what depth is the boy snorkelling?
c What would you find at 6 metres below sea-level?
d At what depth are the dolphins swimming?
e At what height is the paraglider flying?
f What is happening at sea-level?
g The girl playing in the sand wants an ice-cream.
How many metres will she have to climb to get one?
h The boy snorkelling dives down to be beside the shoal of fish.
How many metres does he dive?
i How much lower is the mini-submarine than the scuba divers?

2 Profit and Loss

This graph shows the profit made by the school tuck shop over a period of ten months.

When the tuck shop makes a loss it is shown as a negative profit.

For example, a loss of £25 would be shown as –25 profit.

a The tuck shop made a profit of £3 in April. How well did it do in:
(i) January   (ii) December
(iii) March?
b In which months did it make a loss?
c Which was the worst month for the tuck shop?
d What was the loss in that month?
e By how much did the profits fall between April and May?
f By how much did the profits rise between September and October?

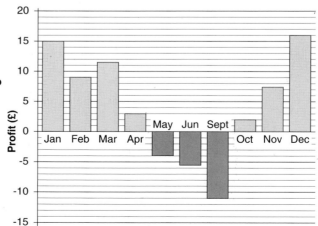

Comparing Scales

EXERCISE 8

1 The **volume** of a liquid can be measured in pints or in millilitres.

We can see which volumes are the same by putting two scales side by side.

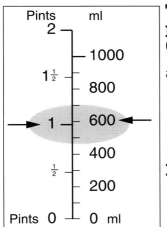

The arrow shows that a **pint** is about the same as **600 ml**.

a Estimate how many millilitres are the same as:
  (i) no pints
  (ii) half a pint
  (iii) one and a half pints.

b Estimate how many pints are the same as 1 litre. (Remember 1 litre = 1000 ml.)

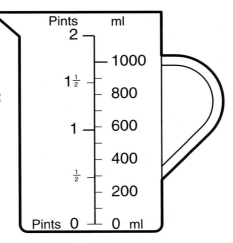

2 **Speed** can be measured in miles per hour or kilometres per hour.

We can see which speeds are the same by putting these two scales together.

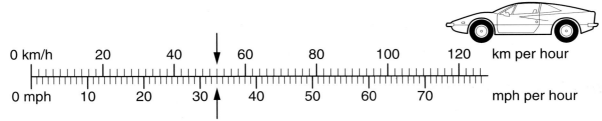

This arrow shows that 33 miles per hour is the same as 52 kilometres per hour.

> Care has to be taken because the top scale 'goes up in twos'and the bottom scale 'goes up in ones'.

Use the scales above to answer these questions.

a What speed in miles per hour is the same as 60 km per hour?
b What speed in km per hour is the same as 70 miles per hour?
c The fastest recorded speed for a lion is 80 km per hour. What is this speed in miles per hour?
d The road in a campsite had a speed limit of 10 miles per hour.
  How fast is this in km per hour?
e The speed limit in most towns is 30 miles per hour. Roughly how fast is this in km per hour?

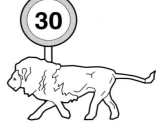

CHECK-UP ON SCALES

1

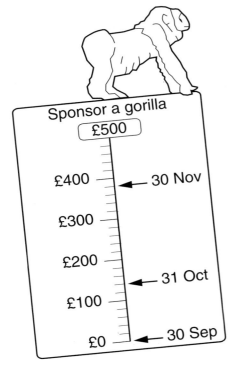

Some pupils are raising money to sponsor a gorilla at the local wildlife park.

They mark the amount raised so far on the last day of each month.

a How much had they raised by 31st October?
b How much had they raised altogether by 30th November?
c How much money did they raise *during* November?
d The pupils want to reach their target by Christmas.
   How much have they still to raise?

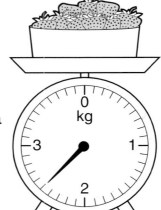

2 Marco is weighing strawberries in a bowl.

The weight of the strawberries and the bowl is shown on the scales.

The bowl weighs 0.7 kg.

How heavy are the strawberries?

3 What is the volume of the orange juice in the measuring jug?

4 Tracey is 1.64 metres tall. How tall is Justin?

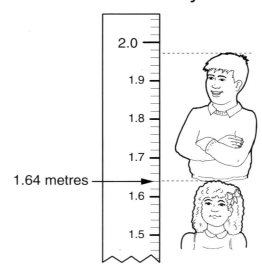

5

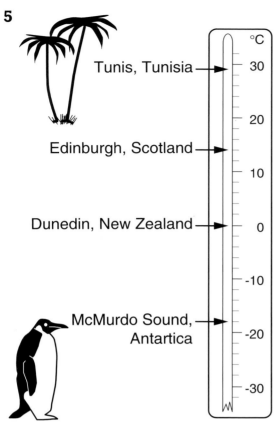

Tunis, Tunisia →

Edinburgh, Scotland →

Dunedin, New Zealand →

McMurdo Sound, Antartica →

The temperatures in four places around the world are recorded on the scale.

a Write down the names of the four places and their temperatures.

b How much warmer was Edinburgh than Dunedin?

c It was 6° cooler in Rome than it was in Tunis.
How warm was it in Rome?

d It was 9° warmer in Santa Cruz than it was in McMurdo Sound.
How warm was it in Santa Cruz?

6

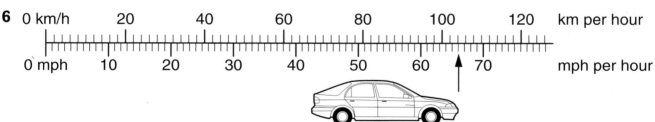

The arrow shows that the car is travelling at 66 miles per hour.

How fast is this in km per hour?

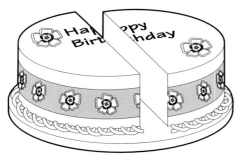 

Two halves   make   a whole.

LOOKING BACK

1 What fraction of each diagram is shaded?

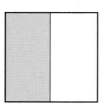

a   **b**   **c**

d   **e**

2 What is: **a** a half of twenty **b** a third of six **c** a quarter of twelve?

3 Work out: **a** $\frac{1}{2}$ of 24   **b** $\frac{1}{3}$ of 33   **c** $\frac{1}{4}$ of 16

4 A dozen eggs means 12 eggs. What is half a dozen?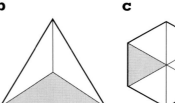

5  The cake weighs 300 grams.
Amy gets $\frac{1}{2}$ of it. Ben gets $\frac{1}{3}$ of it. Colin gets $\frac{1}{6}$ of it.
Work out the weight of each person's share.

6 Asha buys a ticket for a flight to London. It should cost her £50.
There is a discount of £6.
How much does the ticket cost?

$\frac{1}{2} = 1 \div 2 = 0.5$

'of' means ×

Example 1 $\frac{1}{2}$ of 24

On a calculator: 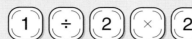 $\boxed{12}$

Example 2 $\frac{1}{3}$ of 15

 $\boxed{5}$

EXERCISE 1

1 **a** Write the following fractions in decimal form. (For example $\frac{1}{2} = 0.5$)
   (i) $\frac{1}{2}$ (ii) $\frac{1}{4}$ (iii) $\frac{1}{5}$ (iv) $\frac{1}{8}$ (v) $\frac{1}{10}$

   b What does your calculator give for:
   (i) $\frac{1}{3}$ (ii) $\frac{1}{6}$ (iii) $\frac{1}{9}$?

2 Work out the following:

   a $\frac{1}{2}$ of 26   **b** $\frac{1}{3}$ of 42   **c** $\frac{1}{4}$ of 36   **d** $\frac{1}{5}$ of 60   **e** $\frac{1}{6}$ of 48   **f** $\frac{1}{7}$ of 42

   g $\frac{1}{8}$ of 72   **h** $\frac{1}{9}$ of 54   **i** $\frac{1}{10}$ of 90   **j** $\frac{1}{11}$ of 22   **k** $\frac{1}{12}$ of 24   **l** $\frac{1}{100}$ of 300

3  $\frac{1}{3}$ of the class cycle to school and the rest walk.

   There are 24 pupils in the class.
   a How many cycle to school?
   b How many walk?

4 Four men run a relay race. The race is 1600 metres long.
   Each man runs a quarter of the race.
   How far does each man run?

5 60 minutes make one hour.
   How many minutes make:
   a half an hour   **b** a quarter of an hour   **c** a third of an hour?

6 100 centimetres make a metre.
   How many centimetres make:
   a half a metre   **b** a quarter of a metre   **c** one fifth of a metre?

$$\frac{2}{5} = 2 \div 5 = 0.4$$

'of' means $\times$

Example $\frac{2}{5}$ of 20

On a calculator:

EXERCISE 2

1 **a** Write the following fractions in decimal form.
(i) $\frac{3}{5}$ (ii) $\frac{3}{4}$ (iii) $\frac{4}{5}$ (iv) $\frac{3}{8}$ (v) $\frac{7}{10}$

   b What does your calculator give for:
(i) $\frac{2}{9}$ (ii) $\frac{5}{9}$ (iii) $\frac{1}{9}$?

2 Work out the following:

   a $\frac{2}{3}$ of 21   **b** $\frac{3}{4}$ of 40   **c** $\frac{5}{6}$ of 36   **d** $\frac{4}{5}$ of 50   **e** $\frac{4}{7}$ of 28   **f** $\frac{3}{7}$ of 14

   g $\frac{3}{8}$ of 40   **h** $\frac{5}{9}$ of 63   **i** $\frac{3}{10}$ of 50   **j** $\frac{7}{10}$ of 20   **k** $\frac{3}{11}$ of 44   **l** $\frac{17}{100}$ of 500

3  $\frac{2}{3}$ of the strawberries in a basket were bruised.

The basket held 900 grams of strawberries.

   a What was the weight of the bruised strawberries?
   b What was the weight of the rest?

4 30 pupils were asked to name their favourite dinosaur.

$\frac{4}{5}$ liked the triceratops.

   a How many liked the triceratops?
   b How many didn't?

5  60 lambs were born on the Manor Farm.

$\frac{9}{10}$ were white and the rest were black.

   a   How many were white?
   b   What fraction were black?
   c   How many were black?

6 Write the following fractions as decimals.

    a $\frac{3}{100}$ **b** $\frac{9}{100}$ **c** $\frac{17}{100}$ **d** $\frac{29}{100}$ **e** $\frac{87}{100}$

7 500 houses were inspected.

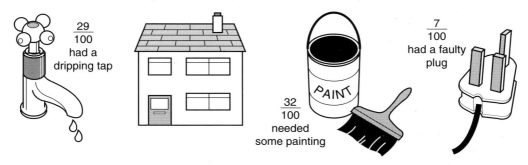

    a How many had a dripping tap?   **b** How many needed painting?

    c How many had a faulty plug?   **d** How many didn't have a faulty plug?

Percentages

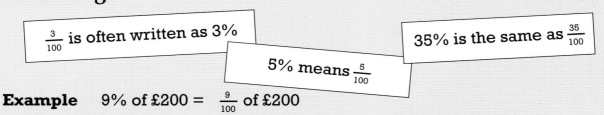

$\frac{3}{100}$ is often written as 3%

5% means $\frac{5}{100}$

35% is the same as $\frac{35}{100}$

Example   9% of £200 = $\frac{9}{100}$ of £200

On a calculator:

EXERCISE 3

1 Write each percentage as a fraction. (For example 5% = $\frac{5}{100}$)

    a 6%   **b** 12%   **c** 36%   **d** 79%   **e** 99%

2 Write each percentage as a decimal fraction.
(For example 5% = 5 ÷ 100 = 0.05)

    a 16%   **b** 28%   **c** 3%   **d** 7%   **e** 69%

3 **a** Write each fraction in decimal form.

       (i) $\frac{1}{2}$ (ii) $\frac{1}{4}$ (iii) $\frac{1}{10}$ (iv) $\frac{1}{5}$

    b Write each percentage in decimal form.

       (i) 25%   (ii) 50%   (iii) 20%   (iv) 10%

    c Now say what fraction is the same as:

       (i) 25%   (ii) 50%   (iii) 20%   (iv) 10%.

4 Work out:
   a 40% of 60 **b** 30% of 90 **c** 50% of 20 **d** 10% of 80
   e 25% of 36 **f** 20% of 10 **g** 100% of 45 **h** 1% of 600

5 A toyshop offers items at 80% of the original cost.
   What is the new cost of each item shown?
   (Remember: when working with £s on a calculator, 1.6 means £1.60.)

a £3 **b** £5 **c** £7 **d** £2

6 The scale model section of the shop is selling items at 60% of the original
   price. What will each of these models cost in the sale?

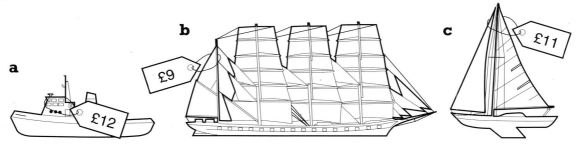

a £12 **b** £9 **c** £11

7 A café offers 10% extra free on all its sales.
   How much extra will you get when you buy:
   a 100 g of chips **b** 300 g of cheese **c** 1000 g of ice-cream?

 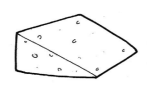 

Discount and Increase

Example 1 A personal stereo costs £48. The shop offers a 10% discount.

   a How much is the discount? $\frac{10}{100} \times 48 = 4.8$
      Discount = £4.80

   b What is the new cost of the stereo?
      New cost = £48 − £4.80 = £43.20

Example 2 Last year a CD cost £14. There has been a 5% increase in costs.
   What is the new cost of the CD? $\frac{5}{100} \times 14 = 0.7$
   Increase = £0.70
   New cost = £14 + £0.70 = £14.70

EXERCISE 4

1 Each of these items is being offered at an 8% discount.
   (i) Work out the discount for each.
   (ii) Find the new price.

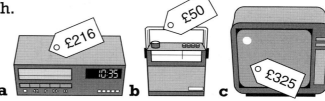

2 The soft toys in a shop are on sale.
   (i) Work out the discount for each.
   (ii) Find the sale price.

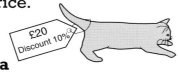

3  Computer discs
£3.00 each
8% discount
if you buy 10

Bryan buys 10 discs.
   a How much would 10 discs normally cost?
   b How much is the discount on 10 discs?
   c How much has Bryan saved on each disc?

4  Calculator
bargains
£4 each

5% discount
if you buy 10
10% discount
if you buy 20

   a The science teacher orders 10 calculators.
      (i) How much would 10 calculators normally cost?
      (ii) What is the price with the discount?
   b The maths teacher buys 20.
      (i) How much would 20 calculators normally cost?
      (ii) What is the price with the discount?

5 A computer store has to put its prices up by 6%.
   Work out: (i) the price increase   (ii) the new price for each item.

   a Computer system   b Printer   c Keyboard

   Old price £600   Old price £2500   Old price £120

6 Work out the new cost of each of these items.

   a   b    c    d

   Toaster was £35   TV was £175   Camera was £105   Phone was £75
   Increase: 5%   Increase: 20%   Increase:15%   Increase: 12%

Profit and Loss

Example 1 Joe bought mugs for £2 each.
He sold them at the market for £2.50.
He made £2.50 – £2.00 = £0.50 **profit** on each mug.

Example 2 He also bought plastic roses for 10p each.
No-one wanted them and he had to sell them at 4p each.
He made 10p – 4p = 6p **loss** on each rose.

Example 3 He bought these globes at £3 each.
He wanted to make 10% profit.
10% of £3 = £0.30
So he sold them for £3 + £0.30 = £3.30 each.

EXERCISE 5

1 Jan ran a tuck shop in school.
 Work out the profit on each item she sold.
 a Crisps (bought for 15p, sold for 25p)
 b Cakes (bought for 13p, sold for 29p)
 c Biscuits (bought for 7p, sold for 15p)
 d Cola (bought for 33p, sold for 46p)
 e Chews (bought for 2p, sold for 9p)
 f Chocolate (bought for 25p, sold for 36p)

2 At the end of term she had to sell the stock off cheaply.
 Work out the loss on each item.
 a Crisps (sold for 12p) **b** Cakes (sold for 9p) **c** Biscuits (sold for 7p)
 d Cola (sold for 25p) **e** Chews (sold for 1p) **f** Chocolate (sold for 20p)

3 Jack bought some items to sell at the market.

 a Pens **b** Notepads **c** Rulers **d** Protractors
 20p each 50p each 30p each 40p each

 He wants to make 10% profit on each item. Work out the selling price of each.

4 The cinema showed a movie about dinosaurs.
 It bought some models to sell. It made a different profit on each model.
 Work out the selling price of each model.

 a Triceratops **b** Diplodocus **c** Stegosaurus **d** T. Rex
 Cost £8 Cost £12 Cost £9 Cost £18
 Profit 10% Profit 8% Profit 12% Profit 15%

Value Added Tax (VAT)

On many things you buy there is an additional cost, a tax called VAT.
This increases the cost of the items by 17.5%.
Usually the marked price includes the VAT.
But look at this advert.

COMPUTER SYSTEM
£450
exc. VAT

VAT has not
been included
in the price.

This works out the VAT.

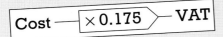

Cost —— ×0.175 — VAT

450 × 0.175 = 78.75
You pay £78.75 VAT
when you buy the computer.

This works out the cost
after the VAT is added.

Cost —— ×1.175 — Cost + VAT

450 × 1.175 = 528.75
You actually pay £528.75
when you buy the computer

EXERCISE 6

1 Work out the VAT you pay on items which cost (before VAT):
   a £12   **b** £26   **c** £56   **d** £2   **e** £124   **f** £98   **g** £10 000

2 Work out what you actually pay on items marked with these prices
   (excluding VAT):
   a £122   **b** £318   **c** £72   **d** £4   **e** £188   **f** £60   **g** £2000

3 Peter saw two adverts for the same calculator.
   (i) £4.80 including VAT   (ii) £4.60 excluding VAT

   a Work out the actual cost of the calculator in the second advert.
   b Which advert offers the better buy?

4 Here is an extract from a catalogue selling computer programs.
   Notice the line 'Prices do not include VAT'.

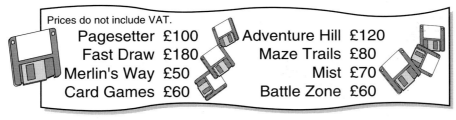

Prices do not include VAT.
Pagesetter £100   Adventure Hill £120
Fast Draw £180   Maze Trails £80
Merlin's Way £50   Mist £70
Card Games £60   Battle Zone £60

Work out the actual cost of each program.

CHECK-UP ON FRACTIONS AND PERCENTAGES

1 Write as decimal fractions: **a** $\frac{1}{8}$ **b** $\frac{1}{16}$

2 Work out the value of **a** $\frac{1}{3}$ of 18   **b** $\frac{1}{5}$ of 55

3 Write as decimal fractions: **a** $\frac{5}{8}$ **b** $\frac{3}{5}$

4 Work out the value of: **a** $\frac{2}{3}$ of 30   **b** $\frac{3}{5}$ of 35

5 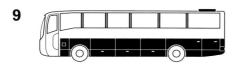 There are 21 books on the shelf.
$\frac{3}{7}$ of the books are maths books.

     a How many are maths books?
     b How many are not?

6 Write each percentage as a fraction: **a** 13%   **b** 37%

7 Write each percentage as a decimal fraction: **a** 43%   **b** 71%

8 Work out the value of: **a** 30% of 30   **b** 50% of 90

9  The bus has 60 seats. 55% of them are booked.

     a How many are booked?
     b How many are not booked?

10 The café usually sells hotdogs for £1.48.
It offers a 25% discount.

     a How much is the discount on a hotdog?
     b What is the new price of a hotdog?

11  The taxi fare down town was £5. It went up by 6%.

     a How big was this increase?
     b What was the new fare?

12 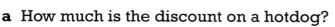 A shop sells sandwiches. It costs 87p to make
one sandwich. They sell the sandwich for £1.50.
How much profit do they make?

13  In a school Enterprise scheme pupils can make badges
at a cost of 90p each. They wish to make 10% profit.

     a How much profit is this on one badge?
     b What is the selling price of a badge?

14 A meal for two at a restaurant costs £22 before VAT.

     a How much VAT has to be paid?   **b** What is the total bill?

7 ANGLE

Do you feel
at home
with angles?

LOOKING BACK

1 How many right angles are there in each of these shapes?

a

b

c

d

e

2 Copy and complete the table for these angles.

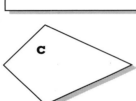

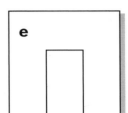

	Angle
Acute	a
Right	
Obtuse	
Straight	

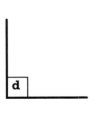

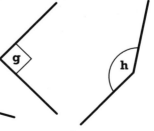

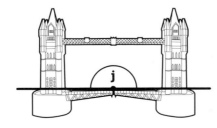

3 Measure these angles.

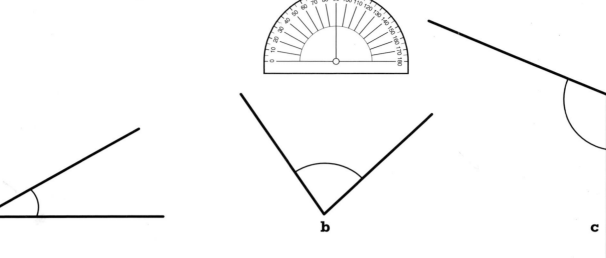

a   **b**   **c**

4 a To make an accurate drawing
of this triangle follow the steps.

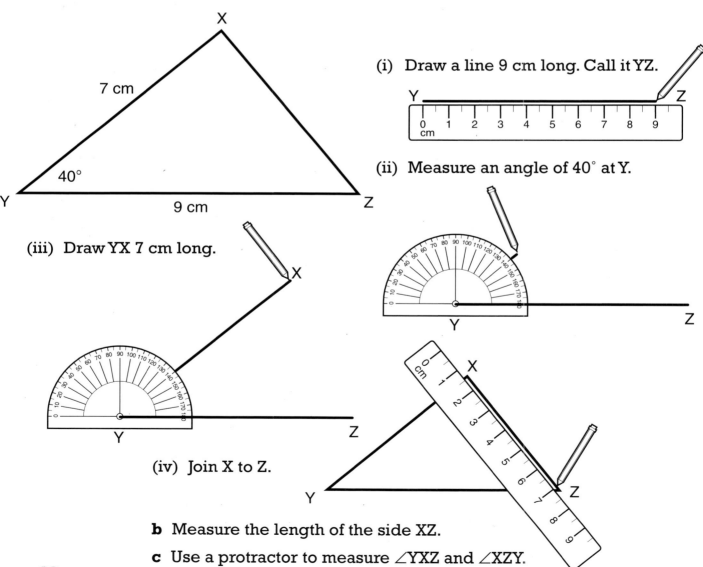

(i) Draw a line 9 cm long. Call it YZ.

(ii) Measure an angle of 40° at Y.

(iii) Draw YX 7 cm long.

(iv) Join X to Z.

b Measure the length of the side XZ.

c Use a protractor to measure ∠YXZ and ∠XZY.

Remember

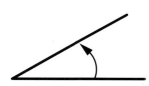

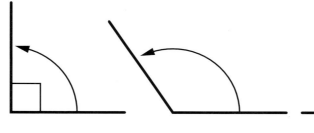

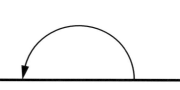

An acute angle is less than 90°.

A right angle is 90°.

An obtuse angle is more than 90° but less than 180°.

A straight angle is 180°.

Some angles measure **more** than 180°.

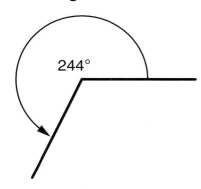

244°

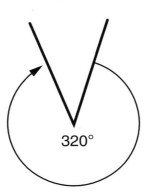

320°

These angles are called **reflex** angles.

EXERCISE 1

1 Which of these angles are **reflex angles**?

a

b

c

d

e

f

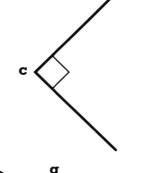

g

h

i

j

2 Copy and complete the table.

	Acute	Right	Obtuse	Straight	Reflex
34°	✔				
126°			✔		
85°					

34°

126°

85°

173°   204°   300°   90°   253°   94°   187°   133°

180°   340°

3 Copy and complete the table for these angles.

	Angle
Acute	
Right	
Obtuse	
Straight	a
Reflex	

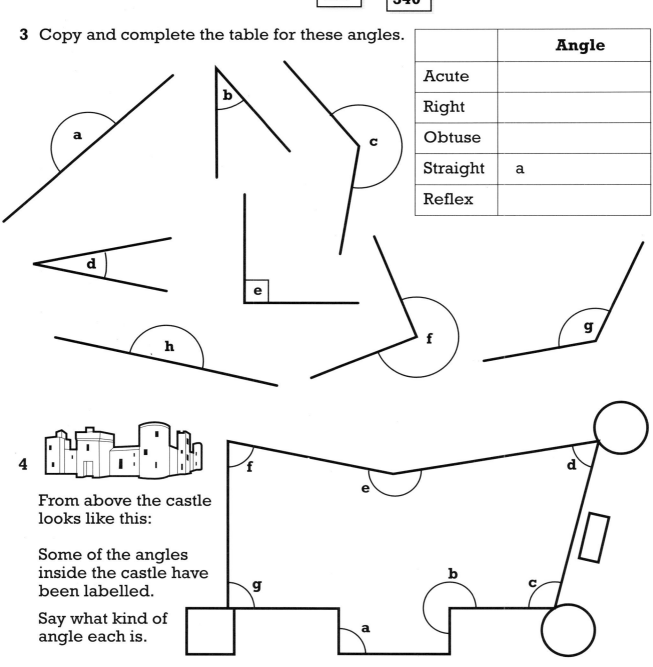

4 From above the castle looks like this:

Some of the angles inside the castle have been labelled.

Say what kind of angle each is.

5 Estimate the size of each marked angle.
Say whether it is acute, right, obtuse, straight or reflex.

Missing Angles

A straight angle is 180°.

180°

If we break a straight angle into two parts ...   ... we can find the missing angle.

$180 - 60 = 120$

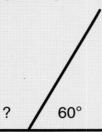

?   60°

120°   60°

EXERCISE 2

1 Calculate the missing angle in each diagram.

a

?   90°

b

?   145°

c

?   72°

d

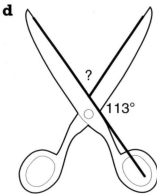

?
113°

e

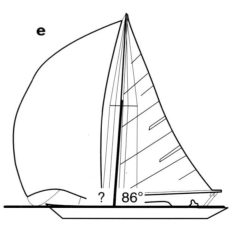

?   86°

f

137°
?

2 Write down the name of each missing angle. Work out its size.

a

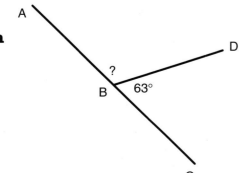

A

D

?
B   63°

C

b

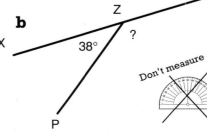

Y

Z
X   38°   ?

P

Don't measure

A right angle is 90°.
If we break a right
angle into two parts ...

? 70°

... we can find the
missing angle.

$$90 - 70 = 20$$

20° 70°

3 What size is the
missing angle?

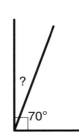

40° ?

4 Calculate the missing angle in each diagram.

a

45° ?

b

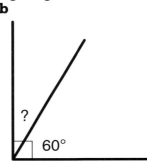

? 60°

c

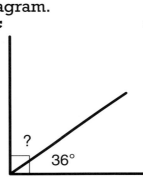

? 36°

d

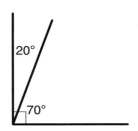

Up

75° ? Down

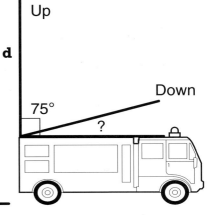

e

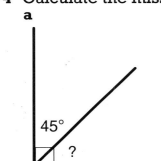

? 81°

f

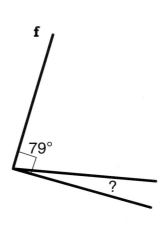

79° ?

g

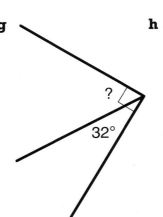

? 32°

h

Horizontal

35° ?

Vertical

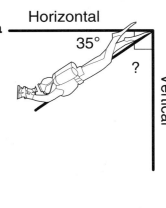

5 Write down the name of each missing angle. Work out its size.

a

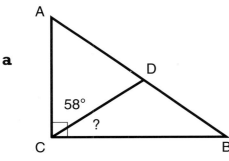

A

D

58° ?

C B

b

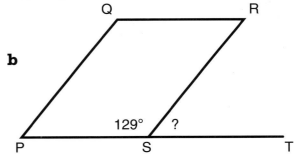

Q R

P 129° ? S T

A Complete Turn

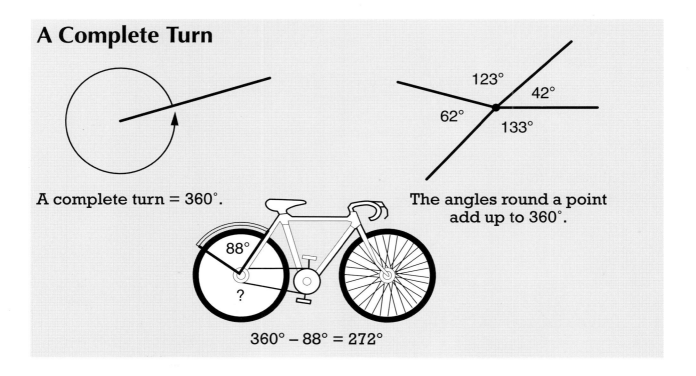

A complete turn = 360°.

The angles round a point add up to 360°.

123°
42°
62°
133°

88°
?

360° − 88° = 272°

EXERCISE 3

1 What size is the missing angle?

90° | 90°
90° | ?

2 How many 45° angles make a complete turn?

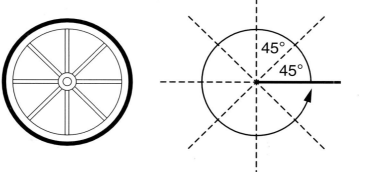

45°
45°

3 There are 16 equal angles. What is the size of each?

4 How many:
   a 30° angles make a complete turn?
   b 90° angles make a complete turn?
   c 180° angles fit round a point?
   d 40° angles fit round a point?
   e 10° angles fit round a point?

5 What size of angle is needed to make up the complete turn?

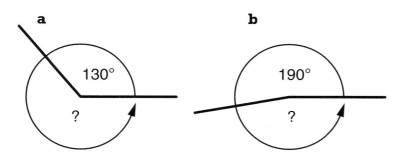

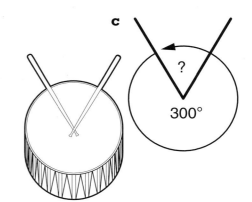

a 130° ?
b 190° ?
c ? 300°

6 What size are the missing angles?

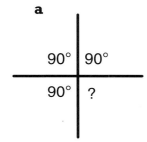
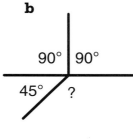
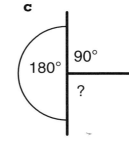
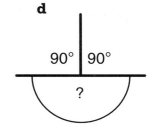

a 90° 90° 90° ?
b 90° 90° 45° ?
c 180° 90° ?
d 90° 90° ?

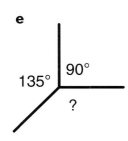
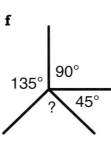
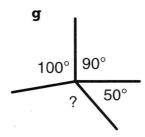
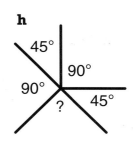

e 135° 90° ?
f 135° 90° ? 45°
g 100° 90° ? 50°
h 45° 90° 90° ? 45°

7 Find the missing angles from:
   a the back wheel
   b the front wheel.

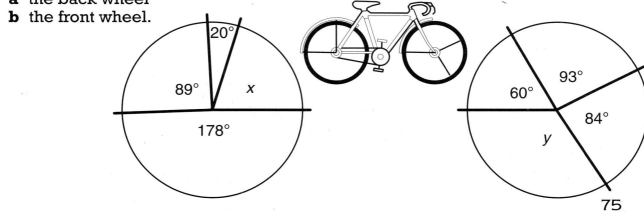

20° 89° x 178°

60° 93° 84° y

8 What is the size of the missing angle?

a

170° | 135°

?

b

120° | 150°

?

c

50°

?

80°

150°

d

55° | ?

65°

115°

45°

55°

9 These circles have been divided into
equal segments.
What is the size of the angles in the centre
of each circle?

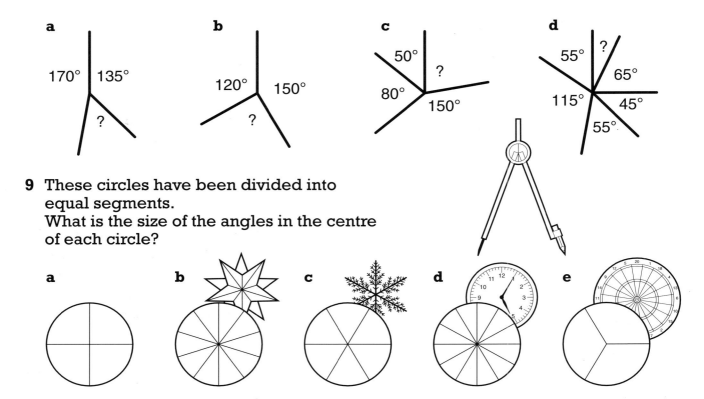

a   **b**   **c**   **d**   **e**

⭐ **Angles in a Triangle**

Measure the angles of this triangle.
Copy and complete:

∠ABC = ...°

∠BAC = ...°

∠ACB = ...°

∠ABC + ∠BAC + ∠ACB = ...°

The angles of a triangle
add up to 180°.

A

B

C

EXERCISE 4

1 Measure the sizes of the angles in each triangle.
Check that in each case the sum is 180°.

a

b

2 Find the size of the missing angle in this triangle by subtracting from 180°.

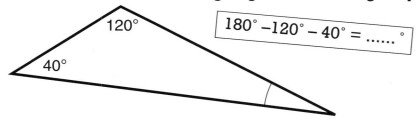

$$180° - 120° - 40° = \ldots\ldots °$$

3 Calculate the size of the missing angles in these triangles.

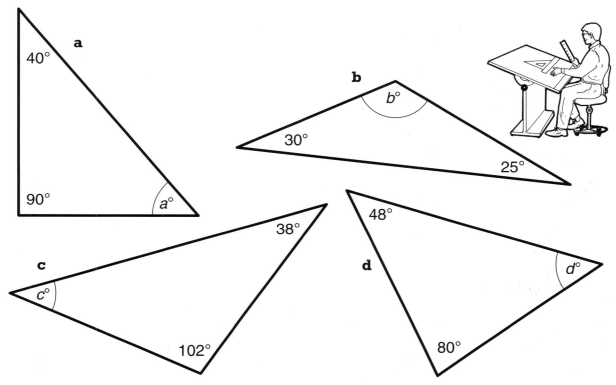

4 (i) Make accurate drawings of these triangles.
(ii) Measure the size of each angle and the length of each side.
(iii) Write the sizes you find in your drawings.

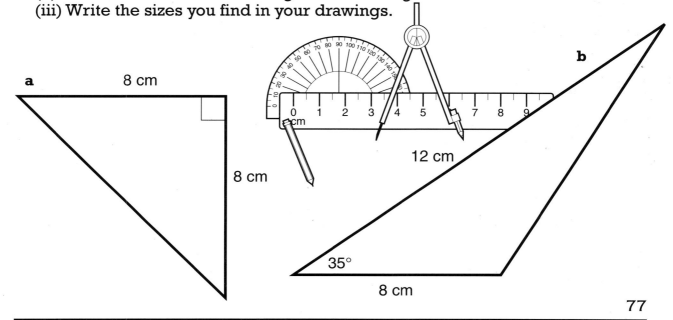

5 These are special triangles.

What is the size of the missing angle in each?

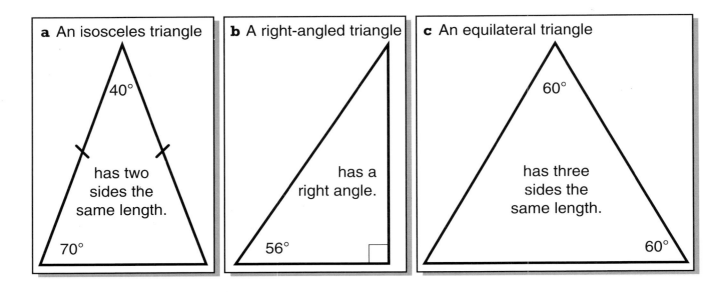

a An isosceles triangle

40°

has two
sides the
same length.

70°

b A right-angled triangle

has a
right angle.

56°

c An equilateral triangle

60°

has three
sides the
same length.

60°

6 Name the missing angle in each of these triangles and give its size.

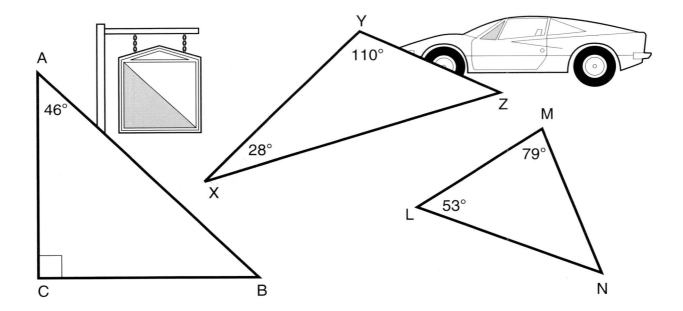

A

46°

C

B

Y

110°

28°

X

Z

M

79°

53°

L

N

CHECK -UP ON ANGLE

1 (i) Estimate the size of each angle.
(ii) Say whether it is acute, right, obtuse, straight or reflex.

a **b** **c** **d** **e**

2 Which of these angles are reflex angles?

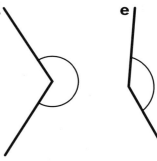

3 What is the size of the missing angle in each diagram?

a **b** **c** **d**

? 145° ? 30° 63° ? ? 59°

4 a How many 90° angles make a **complete turn**?
b How many 60° angles fit round a point?
c How many 180° angles are in 360°?

5 What size are the missing angles?

a **b** **c**

90° 90°
? 135°

45°
180° ?

100° 90°
? 50°

6 What size are the missing angles?

a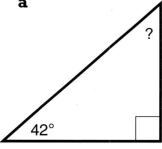

42°

b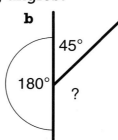

Y
35°
113°
X
? Z

c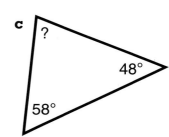

?
48°
58°

LOOKING BACK

1 **5th June 1996** can be written as **05.06.96.**
Write these dates in the same way:

   a 18th March 1995   **b** 3rd October 1998   **c** 20th August 1990

2 Write these dates using the name of the month:

   a 26.09.98   **b** 13.05.99   **c** 30.11.97

3 Write in words the time shown on each clock:

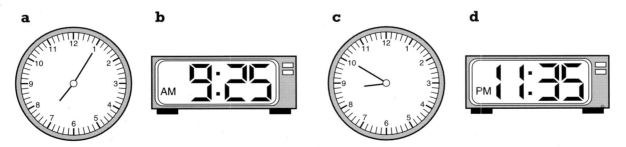

4 Write these times as 12-hour times with am or pm:

   a 06 30   **b** 14 00   **c** 15 30   **d** 18 50

5 Rewrite your answers to question **4** in **words**, using the phrase 'in the morning', 'in the afternoon' or 'in the evening'.

6 Write these as 24-hour times:

a 4.30 am   **b** 1 pm   **c** 7.40 pm   **d** a quarter to seven in the morning

7 How long is the café open?

The Mad Hatter's Café

Opens: 12.15 pm.
Closes: 11.00 pm.

8

WANTED
Shop Assistant for **Saturday**

08 20 until 17 30

How many hours of work is this?

9 This is part of a bus timetable:

Craigie	14 15
Newton	14 23
Doonfast	14 35
Dunure	15 05
Kirkmichael	15 34

a How long does the bus take from Craigie to Newton?
b How long does it take from Craigie to Kirkmichael?
c How long is it from Newton to Dunure?
d I am waiting for the bus in Dunure.
The time on the church clock is a quarter past two.
How long is it until the bus comes?

The Calendar

Some manufacturers put a six-figure code on their packets and tins.

Example
03 11 95 means the flakes were packed on the 3rd of November 1995.

EXERCISE 1

1 a When were these goods packed?

(i)   (ii)   (iii)

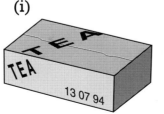

13 07 94

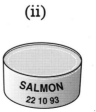

SALMON
22 10 93

SALT
26 03 94

b What dates do these codes represent?

(i) 31 03 92   (ii) 11 11 91   (iii) 22 02 92   (iv) 30 03 90

c What code would be put on goods packed on:

(i) 9th August 1991   (ii) 23rd April 1996   (iii) 12th December 1992?

2 The 3rd of June was a Saturday.

a Copy and complete the pages from the calendar.

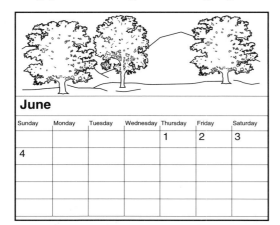

June						
Sunday	Monday	Tuesday	Wednesday	Thursday	Friday	Saturday
				1	2	3
4						

July						
Sunday	Monday	Tuesday	Wednesday	Thursday	Friday	Saturday

b What day of the week is:

(i) 17th June   (ii) 9th June   (iii) 12th June   (iv) 3rd July   (v) 20th July?

3 a On what day of the week is Christmas Day?

b How many Saturdays are in this December? How many Sundays are there?

c School holidays begin after Friday 18th. How many school days are there in December?

d Mary works in a café on Monday and Tuesday evenings. How many evenings does she work in December?

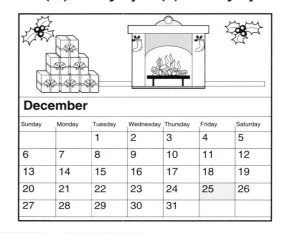

December						
Sunday	Monday	Tuesday	Wednesday	Thursday	Friday	Saturday
		1	2	3	4	5
6	7	8	9	10	11	12
13	14	15	16	17	18	19
20	21	22	23	24	25	26
27	28	29	30	31		

Example 1

SCHOOL TRIP TO FRANCE
Leave: 4th May
Arrive Home: 9th May

30 days has September
April, June and November.
All the rest have 31
Except February alone
Which has 28 days clear
And 29 in each leap year.

How many days were the pupils away?

4th May	1 day	
4th May to 5th May	2 days	notice 5 – 4 = 1
4th May to 6th May	3 days	notice 6 – 4 = 2
4th May to 7th May	4 days	notice 7 – 4 = 3
4th May to 8th May	5 days	notice 8 – 4 = 4
4th May to 9th May	6 days	notice 9 – 4 = 5

If the dates are in one month, **subtract the two dates and add 1**.

Example 2

Holidays start on 28th June and finish on 17th August.
How many days of holiday is this?

> If there is more than one month, **take each month separately and then add**.

June: 28th to 30th June	(30 − 28 = 2;	2 + 1 = 3)	3 days
July: 1st to 31st July	(31 − 1 = 30;	30 + 1 = 31)	31 days
August: 1st to 17th August	(17 − 1 = 16;	16 + 1 = 17)	17 days
Total number of days		=	51

EXERCISE 1B

1 How many days are there here?

a From 4th May to 16th June
b From 29th October to 3rd December
c From 20th September to 5th November
d From 25th November to 10th January

NOVEMBER
JANUARY

2

a Herbie went to the USA on 7th August and came home on 28th August.
How many days was he away?

b Sarah went to Spain on 28th June and came back on 14th July.
How long was she away?

c Tom started building his garage on 14th March and finished on 3rd May.
How long did it take him?

d Jenny started a walk for charity on 26th June and finished on 16th September.
For how many days did she walk?

Example

Britain held the Olympic Games in 1948.
How long ago was that?
Subtract 1948 from the current year.
Suppose it is 1999.
If so, the Olympic Games were held in Britain
1999 − 1948 = 51 years ago.

3 How many years ago did these events take place?

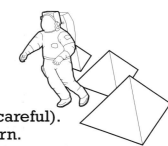

a 1969, men walked on the moon.
b 1945, the end of the Second World War.
c 1066, the Battle of Hastings.
d 55 BC, Julius Caesar landed in Britain from Rome (be careful).
e 582 BC, the Greek mathematician, Pythagoras, was born.
f 2300 BC, pyramids were being built in Egypt.

Working with Units

60 seconds = 1 minute
60 minutes = 1 hour
24 hours = 1 day
52 weeks = 1 year
12 months = 1 year

February

Sunday	Monday	Tuesday	Wednesday	Thursday	Friday	Saturday
		1	2	3	4	5
6	7	8	9	10	11	12
13	14	15	16	17	18	19
20	21	22	23	24	25	26
27	28	29				

EXERCISE 2

1 How many seconds are in:

   a 2 minutes   **b** 5 minutes   **c** 10 minutes   **d** $\frac{1}{2}$ minute   **e** $1\frac{1}{2}$ minutes?

2 How many minutes are in:

   a 2 hours   **b** 4 hours   **c** $\frac{1}{2}$ hour

   d $1\frac{1}{2}$ hours   **e** 180 seconds   **f** 150 seconds?

3 How many hours are in:

   a 2 days   **b** a week   **c** $\frac{1}{2}$ day

   d $\frac{1}{4}$ day   **e** 90 minutes   **f** 180 minutes?

4 David walks to Hillhouse, then to
Fairhaven and back home.
The time for each part of the
journey is shown.

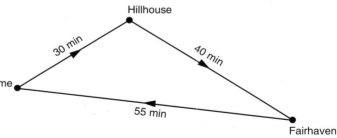

   a How long did David walk?

      Give your answer in: (i) minutes   (ii) hours and minutes.

   b How long does it take to get home from Hillhouse (in hours and minutes)?

   c David started the walk at noon. When did he arrive back home?

5 The buses from Carrick to Doon run every 20 minutes.
The first one in the morning leaves Carrick at 06 00.
It arrives in Doon at 06 35.
Copy and complete the timetable for the first four buses.

	Bus 1	Bus 2	Bus 3	Bus 4
Carrick (depart)	06 00	06 20		
Doon (arrive)	06 35			

6 Melanie has bought The Gargles' new CD.
There are five tracks.
The first one lasts for 5 minutes and 15 seconds (5' 15").

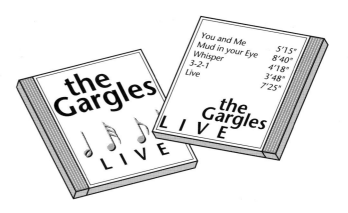

You and Me	5'15"
Mud in your Eye	8'40"
Whisper	4'18"
3-2-1	3'48"
Live	7'25"

  a What is the total playing time of the CD?

  b What is the difference in playing time between the longest and shortest songs?

7

Brian has a three-hour videotape.
He tapes these programmes:

Top of the Pops   30 minutes
Sybil's Kitchen   45 minutes
Wildlife in Britain 50 minutes
Dancing Shoes   40 minutes

How many minutes of tape are left?

Intervals

| Mid-night | 1 | 2 | 3 | 4 | 5 | 6 | 7 | 8 | 9 | 10 | 11 | 12 | 1 | 2 | 3 | 4 | 5 | 6 | 7 | 8 | 9 | 10 | 11 | Mid-night |

Example

A television programme lasted from 6.15 pm to 8.45 pm.
How long was that?

Use the time-line to help you find the answer.

6.15 to 7.15 to 8.15 is 2 hours.
8.15 to 8.45 is 30 minutes.

The total time was 2 hours and 30 minutes.

EXERCISE 3

1 a In school, the morning interval is from 10.55 am until 11.15 am.
    How long is the interval?

  b The lunch-break starts at 11.55 am and finishes at 1 pm.
    How long is this?

2 A new play is on at the Church Theatre.

    a How long is the interval?

    b How long is it from the start of
       Act 1 until the end of Act 2?

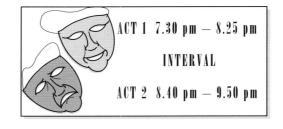

ACT 1 7.30 pm – 8.25 pm

INTERVAL

ACT 2 8.40 pm – 9.50 pm

3 Jenny arrives at the
bus-stop at:

How long did Jenny
have to wait for the
bus?

The bus
comes at:

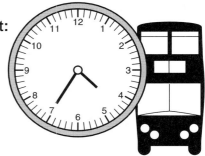

4 A shop opens
at:

08:45

and closes
at:
17:30

How long is the shop open?

5 The right time is twenty-five to eight.

Adam's watch is 10 minutes fast.
Bindoo's watch is 3 minutes slow.

Copy and complete:

    a Carol's watch is ... minutes ...
    b Dean's watch is ... minutes ...
    c Ed's watch is ... minutes ...
    d Fiona's watch is ... minutes ...

Adam's watch   Bindoo's watch
7:32

Carol's watch   Dean's watch
7:40

Ed's watch   Fiona's watch
7:54

Leap Years

A year is the time it takes the Earth to go round the sun.
It takes 365 and a quarter days.
So we have three years with 365 days and then one
with 366 days.
Every fourth year, February is given an extra day
(the 29th).
We say every fourth year is a leap year.

> **A year is a leap year if its last two digits can be divided by 4.**

Example 1 1984 is a leap year because 84 can be divided by 4.
Example 2 1990 is not a leap year because 90 cannot be divided by 4.

EXERCISE 4

1 Which of these are leap years?

    a 1982   **b** 1988   **c** 1996   **d** 1998   **e** 1950   **f** 2004

2 How many days are there in these years?

    a 1940   **b** 1960   **c** 1970   **d** 1975   **e** 1978   **f** 1992

3 How many days are there from the beginning of January until the end of
February in:

    a 1980   **b** 1998   **c** 2002?

4 Which years were leap years in the 1970s?

5 The Olympic Games are held in leap years.

    a Which of these could be Olympic years?
        (i) 1948   (ii) 1950   (iii) 1988   (iv) 1998
    b When will the next Olympic Games be held?
    c When will the first Games be held after 2010?

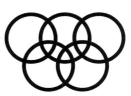

6  The World Cup soccer tournament is held every four years.
It is held two years after the Olympic Games.
In 1994 the tournament was held in the USA.

    a Which of the following are World Cup years?
        (i) 1950   (ii) 1964   (iii) 1974
    b When is the next World Cup?
    c When is the first World Cup after 2010?

7 How many leap years have there been since you were born? Can you list them?

Timetables

Sally made a timetable of some of the things she did on Monday.

Sally's day	Time
Got up	8.00 am
Left for school	8.45 am
Arrived at school	9.00 am
Lunch-break	12.15 pm
Went back to classes	1.00 pm
Left school	3.30 pm
Arrived home	3.45 pm
Had tea	5.30 pm
Did homework	7.00 pm
Watched TV	8.30 pm
Went to bed	11.45 pm

EXERCISE 5

1 a How long does it take Sally to travel to school?
  b How long is the lunch-break?
  c   (i) When did Sally arrive in school?
      (ii) When did she leave?
      (iii) How long was she in school?
  d How long did Sally watch TV?

2 Make a timetable like Sally's for one of your recent school days.

3 Here is a copy of Sally's weekly timetable:

	9.00–9.15	9.15–10.10	10.10–11.05		11.20–12.15		1.00–2.00	2.00–3.00
Period	1	2	3		4		5	6
Monday	Assembly	English	Science	Interval	Music	Lunch	Maths	Home Economics
Tuesday	Assembly	PE	Maths	Interval	Technical	Lunch	Social Subjects	French
Wednesday	Assembly	French	English	Interval	Guidance	Lunch	Social Subjects	Computing
Thursday	Assembly	Science	Home Economics	Interval	French	Lunch	PE	Technical
Friday	Assembly	Maths	Social Subjects	Interval	English	Lunch	Science	Art

  a Are all the periods the same length? Explain.
  b When is the morning interval? How long is it?
  c She studied English for three periods.
     Make a similar statement about all the subjects Sally studies.
     (Check that the periods add up to 25.)
  d How many hours and minutes does each subject get?

4 Repeat question **3** for your own timetable.

The Westland Bus Company issues this timetable of buses running between Gailes and Skares in the morning.

Gailes	06 30	07 00	07 30	08 00	08 30	09 00
Loans	06 42	07 12	07 42	08 12	08 42	09 12
Monkton	06 52	07 22	07 52	08 22	08 52	09 22
Heathfield	06 58	07 28	07 58	08 28	08 58	09 28
Coylton	07 14	07 44	08 14	08 44	09 14	09 44
Skares	07 23	07 53	08 23	08 53	09 23	09 53

Beat the rush hour – go by bus.

EXERCISE 6

1 Mike lives in Loans and works in Coylton. He travels by bus to his work.

 a How often does the bus run from Gailes to Skares?
 b How long does the bus take to go from Gailes to Skares?
 c How long does it take Mike to go from Loans to Coylton?
 d Mike starts his work at half past eight.
  What bus will he need to catch from Loans?

2 Mike works for Solar Chips plc. He needs to 'clock-in' and 'clock-out' each day. His timecard for last week is shown.

 a What do you think are the normal daily working hours for Mike?
 b How many mornings is he 'late'?
 c Copy and complete Mike's timecard.

Mike Muir Employee Number 247 Dept E Week 15			Total	
	Time in	Time out	hours	mins
Monday	08 28	17 35	9	7
Tuesday	08 31	17 34		
Wednesday	08 27	17 38		
Thursday	08 24	17 32		
Friday	08 35	17 30		
Weekly total				

3 At night Mike likes to relax in front of his TV.

BBC 1
5.35 Neighbours
6.00 Six o'clock News
6.30 Local News
7.00 Top of the Pops
7.30 Eastenders
8.00 Beechgrove Garden

BBC 2
4.30 Darts
6.00 Film: The Last Voyage
7.30 Old School Ties
8.00 African Days
8.30 Nightmares
9.00 Likely Lads

Channel 3
5.10 Emmerdale
5.40 ITN News
6.00 Home and Away
7.00 Bing Hope Show
7.30 Big Story
8.00 The Bill

Channel 4
5.00 Looneytoons
6.00 Home Improvements
6.30 Roseanne
7.00 Channel 4 News
7.50 The Switch
8.00 Visions

 a Are these times am or pm?
 b Which channel has a programme starting at 7.50?
 c How long does the BBC2 film last?
 d Mike watches all of *Emmerdale* and then switches over to catch *Neighbours*. How much of *Neighbours* does he miss?
 e He switched channels again 10 minutes before the end of the 6 o'clock news. What time was that?

CHECK-UP ON TIME

1 a Copy and complete this calendar for November.

  b (i) How many Saturdays are in November?

     (ii) How many Mondays are there?

  c On what day of the week:

     (i) is 5th December

     (ii) was 28th October?

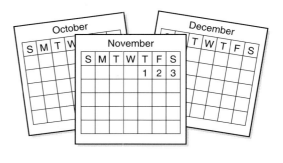

2 Tom and Tracy write their dates of birth:

 Tom 09.10.83   Tracy 29.02.84

  a Write their dates of birth in words.

  b What can you say about the year 1984?

  c (i) Who is older, Tom or Tracy?

     (ii) By how many months?

3 How many days are their from 8th July to 12th August? (Count both the first and last dates.)

4 Bert took 3 hours and 40 minutes to paint his side of the fence.

Mildred took 3 hours and 25 minutes to paint her side.

  a What was the total time taken?

  b What is the difference in their times?

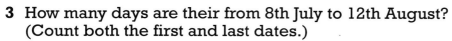

5 Gaffur waited 8 minutes for the bus to leave. How many seconds is this?

6 'The flight for Paris is delayed by 90 minutes.' The plane was due to leave at 08 15. When will the plane leave?

7 Which of these years is a leap year?
  a 1994   **b** 1996
Explain your answer.

8 Write each of these times as:
  (i) a 12-hour time with am or pm
  (ii) a 24-hour time.
    a half past two in the morning
    b three o'clock in the afternoon
    c twenty past eleven in the morning
    d quarter to seven in the evening

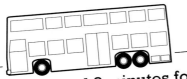

9

POP CONCERT

The Screamers	9.30 pm – 9.45 pm
The Ravers	9.45 pm – 10.10 pm
Shoe Shine Boys	10.10 pm – 11.30 pm

How long did each group perform?

10

The West Highland Line

Glasgow (Queen Street)	08 42
Dalmuir	08 57
Helensburgh	09 25
Ardlui	10 12
Upper Tyndrum	10 17
Rannoch	10 52
Fort William arrive	11 49
depart	12 00
Glenfinnan	12 32
Mallaig	13 20

The West Highland Railway Line runs from Glasgow to Mallaig.
Part of the timetable is shown.

a How long does it take from Glasgow to Dalmuir?
b How long does the train stop at Fort William?
c How long is the journey from Glenfinnan to Mallaig?
d Calculate the time for the whole journey from Glasgow to Mallaig.

9 CHARTS AND TABLES

Four puppies had their weights and lengths measured.

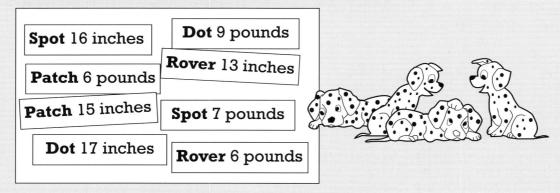

Spot 16 inches   Dot 9 pounds

Patch 6 pounds   Rover 13 inches

Patch 15 inches   Spot 7 pounds

Dot 17 inches   Rover 6 pounds

It often helps to organise information into a table.

Dog's name	Length in inches	Weight in pounds
Dot	17	9
Patch	15	6
Rover	13	6
Spot	16	7

It is now easier to answer questions about the puppies.

Example: How heavy is Rover?
Think! What are we looking for?
- Rover
- Weight

Look along the 'Rover' row.
Look down the 'Weight' column.

Dog's name	Length in inches	Weight in pounds
Dot	17	9
Patch	15	6
Rover	13	6
Spot	16	7

Rover is 6 pounds.

EXERCISE 1

Use the table above to answer these questions.
1 **a** How long is Patch?
   b How heavy is Spot?
   c (i) Which puppy is the longest?
       (ii) How long is it?
   d (i) Which puppy is the heaviest?
       (ii) How heavy is it?
   e Which two puppies are the same weight?
   f What is the total weight of the four puppies?

2 This table was printed in a newspaper.
It shows the rainfall and the hours of sunshine around Scotland on one day.

	Sunshine in hours	Rainfall in centimetres
Aberdeen	6.2	0.7
Aviemore	8.7	nil
Eskdalemuir	5.8	1.3
Kinloss	7.9	0.1
Tiree	8.2	0.2

a How much rain was there in Kinloss?
b Which town was the sunniest?
c Which town had no rain?
d How many more hours of sunshine did Tiree get than Eskdalemuir?

3 This table shows the temperatures recorded around Scotland one day.
The temperatures are in degrees Celsius (°C).

Place name	Maximum temperature	Minimum temperature
Aberdeen	18 °C	7 °C
Edinburgh	20 °C	12 °C
Glasgow	19 °C	13 °C
Oban	21 °C	8 °C
Stranraer	17 °C	10 °C

Use the table to answer these questions.

a What was the maximum temperature in Glasgow?

b (i) Which town had the lowest temperature?
   (ii) What was that temperature?

c What was the minimum temperature in Edinburgh?

d (i) Which town had the highest maximum temperature?
   (ii) What was that temperature?

e What is the difference between the maximum and minimum temperatures in Stranraer?

Advertisements

Many adverts give information in the form of a table.
This advert shows the cost of four cars.

KUANU CARS

Special Price until July	Saloon	Estate
Siesta 1.3	£8500	£9250
Siesta 1.8 GTI	£11 760	£13 340

Example
Find the cost of a Siesta 1.8 GTI Estate.
Think! What are we looking for?
  • Siesta 1.8 GTI
  • Estate
Look along the Siesta 1.8 GTI row.
Look down the Estate column.
It costs £13 340.

	Saloon	Estate
Siesta 1.3	£8500	£9250
Siesta 1.8 GTI	£11 760	►£13 340

EXERCISE 2

1   The Tower Hotel placed this advert in a national newspaper.

FULL BOARD

Summer Prices	Adult prices per person	Child prices (up to 12 years of age)
1 night	£55	£30
2 nights	£105	£50
7 nights	£280	£130

   a Stephen, an accountant, spends one night in the Tower Hotel.
   How much does it cost?
   b Jack and Sarah McCall spent seven nights in the hotel.
   How much did it cost them?
   c Mr and Mrs Preston and their daughter, aged 8, stay for
   two nights. Work out the total bill for the family.
   d Khalid and Irma came to the hotel on their honeymoon.
   Their bill was £210.
   For how many nights did they stay?
   e Tony, Sue and their children stayed at the hotel for seven nights.
   All the children were under 12. The total bill was £820.
   How many children do they have?

2 This advert shows the cost of crossing the Channel to France with two different ferry companies.

	May	June	July	August
P & Q Ferries	£120	£192	£280	£292
Sea-Craft Ferries	£130	£190	£310	£325

Cost is for 1 car and up to 5 passengers.

a The Crosby family travel to France in June.
They go with P & Q Ferries.
How much does it cost?

b Mr and Mrs Eribe take their holidays in August.
They travel to France by Sea-Craft Ferries.
How much does it cost?

c Carrie and her two friends want to visit France in July.
They would like the cheapest crossing.
(i) Which ferry company should they chose?
(ii) How much will it cost?

d The Stanger family's crossing cost £292.
(i) Which company did they use?
(ii) In which month did they travel?

e Sally, Catriona, Rachel and Claire travel to France in May.
They sail with Sea-Craft Ferries.
They share the cost of the journey between them.
How much do they each pay?

3 The Holiday Car Hire Company placed this advert in a holiday brochure.

	1 day	3 days	7 days
Car (up to 5 people)	£24	£65	£125
Minibus (8 seater)	£41	£110	£205
4-wheel-drive jeep (up to 5 people)	£34	£92	£180

a How much is it to hire a car for three days?
b How much is it to hire a 4-wheel-drive jeep for a week?
c How much does it cost to hire a minibus for a day?
d The Malik family would like to hire a vehicle for seven days.
How much will they save if they choose a car instead of the jeep?
e There are eight people in the Davies family.
They would like to hire a vehicle for three days.
How much will they save if they hire a minibus instead of two separate cars?

Buy More – Save Money!

Costs often depend upon how many items you buy.
The more you buy, the cheaper each item becomes.

Perfect Pencils
Ideal for school and drawing
1-99 pencils   15 pence each
100 or more   14 pence each

If you want to buy 35 pencils,
you pay 15p each.
Cost: $35 \times 15p = £5.25$

But if you buy 120 pencils,
you pay 14p each.
Cost: $120 \times 14p = £16.80$

EXERCISE 3

1

Flexi-unbreakable Rulers
Measure in centimetres and inches
1-25   45p each
26-50   42p each

a Andrew would like to buy ten rulers.
  (i) How much will he be charged for each ruler?
  (ii) What will he have to pay altogether?

b Mrs Methven is ordering rulers for her class. She orders 30.
  (i) How much will she have to pay for each ruler?
  (ii) What will she pay altogether?

c Work out the cost of buying:
  (i) 45 rulers   (ii) 17 rulers.

2

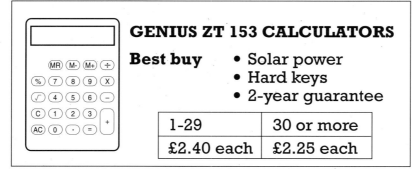

GENIUS ZT 153 CALCULATORS

Best buy   • Solar power
          • Hard keys
          • 2-year guarantee

1-29	30 or more
£2.40 each	£2.25 each

a Mr Platt decides to order these new calculators for his maths class. He orders 25 calculators. How much will they cost altogether?

b Ms Millan orders a calculator for everyone in her office. She needs 12 calculators. How much will they cost?

c Work out the cost of buying:
  (i) 8   (ii) 50   (iii) 29 calculators.

3

United Rugby Shirts

Special Offer

Up to 15   £25.50 each
16+   £24.20 each

a Mrs Hastings buys a new rugby shirt for each of her three sons.
  (i) How much will each shirt cost?
  (ii) What is the total cost of the rugby shirts?
b 'Hawick Fillies' want to buy new rugby shirts for their 15 players and 4 reserves. How much will the shirts cost altogether?
c Esperance Academy decides to replace the school's rugby kit.
They order 55 rugby shirts.
What will be the total cost of the rugby shirts?

4 a Shaya needs 15 copies of a letter.
  (i) How much will each copy cost?
  (ii) How much will Shaya pay altogether?
b Peter and his friends are holding a charity sale.
They order 35 copies of a poster.
How much will it cost for the photocopying?
c Jan needs 8 copies of one letter and 12 copies of another.
Copy and complete the receipt.
d Haley pays £1.84 for her photocopying. How many copies did she get?

Photocopying While You Wait

Number of copies	Price
1-9 copies	10p each
10-19 copies	9p each
20 copies or more	8p each

Photocopying While You Wait

Receipt
8 copies at ...... each =
12 copies at ...... each =
Total =

5 The cost of placing an advert in the *Southern Advertiser* is shown below.

Advertise with the Southern Advertiser.

Not more than 10 words	10p per word
11 words to 20 words	9p per word
21 words or more	8p per word

Work out the cost of placing these adverts in the *Southern Advertiser*.

a

For sale: Lady's bicycle.
Excellent condition.
Telephone 21985.

One word

b

Golden Retriever dog puppy,
6 weeks old.
Excellent pedigree.
Kennel Club registered.
Baillie, Spearbank Farm.

Do Worksheet **1**

c

For sale: Antique (Georgian) chest of drawers.
Very good condition. Mahogany, 5 drawers.
Valued at £3000. First £2500 will secure.
Telephone: 738497.

Ready Reckoners

A ready reckoner will save you doing the same calculations again and again.

Jamie works in a baker's shop.
He uses this ready reckoner to give
him the cost of rolls.
Some answers have been worked out
and written down as a table.

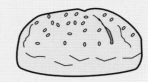

Number of rolls	Cost
1	13p
2	26p
3	39p
4	52p
5	65p
6	78p
7	91p
8	£1.04
9	£1.17
10	£1.30
20	£2.60
30	£3.90
40	£5.20
50	£6.50

Examples

6 rolls cost 78 pence.

28 rolls cost:

20 rolls £2.60
8 rolls £1.04
_____
£3.64

EXERCISE 5

Use the ready reckoner above to answer these questions.

1 Write down the cost of:
  a 4 rolls **b** 7 rolls **c** 30 rolls.

2 Work out the cost of:
  a 13 rolls **b** 45 rolls **c** 37 rolls.

3 Now work out the cost of:
  a 60 rolls **b** 85 rolls **c** 125 rolls.
  Remember to show any working you do.

4 How many rolls could you buy for:
  a 78p **b** £1.56 **c** £8.32?

5 Price increase! Rolls now cost 15p each.
  Make a ready reckoner similar to the
  one above to help Jamie.

Da Worksheet **2**

Da Worksheet **3**

Da Worksheet **4**

CHECK-UP ON CHARTS AND TABLES

1 This table shows the number of calories to be found in certain foods.

Food	Calories per 100 grams
Apple	36
Bread	242
Cheese (Cheddar)	424
Tomato (raw)	14
Ham	218

How many calories would be eaten if:
a Phil eats 100 g of bread
b Susie eats 50 g of ham and 200 g of apple?

2 The cost of putting an advert in the *Edinburgh Times* for one day is shown below.

Daily rates	
1 to 5 lines	£4.10 per line
More than 5 lines	£3.85 per line

Calculate the cost of these adverts:

a

Wanted: Wooden hen house for up to 20 hens. Fully equipped with perches and nest boxes. Good condition essential. Good price paid. Telephone 01234567.

For one day only.

b

For sale: Fridge, two years old. Very good condition. £60 o.n.o. Tel: 01765432.

For three days.

3 **a** How far is it from Belview to Dell?
b Calculate the distance travelled by a van driver who goes from Arrowdale to Dell, then to Eythe and back to Arrowdale.

Arrowdale

76	**Belview**			
52	35	**Comrow**		
27	88	19	**Dell**	
58	41	25	46	**Eythe**
33	70	66	59	61	**Fernville**

Distances in kilometres

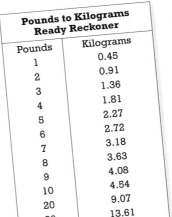

4 Use the ready reckoner to calculate how many kilograms are the same as:

a 7 pounds
b 15 pounds
c 70 pounds
d 135 pounds.

Pounds to Kilograms Ready Reckoner	
Pounds	Kilograms
1	0.45
2	0.91
3	1.36
4	1.81
5	2.27
6	2.72
7	3.18
8	3.63
9	4.08
10	4.54
20	9.07
30	13.61
40	18.14
50	22.68
100	45.40

10 GRAPHS

LOOKING BACK

1 A rock group's albums were on sale after a concert.
   This pictograph shows the sales.

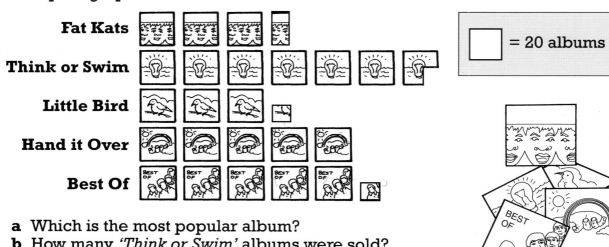

Fat Kats

Think or Swim

Little Bird

Hand it Over

Best Of

$\square$ = 20 albums

a Which is the most popular album?
b How many *'Think or Swim'* albums were sold?
c How many copies were sold of the least popular album?
d Which albums sold more than 100 copies?

2 This bar graph shows a week's sales of coffee in Kelly's Coffee Shop.

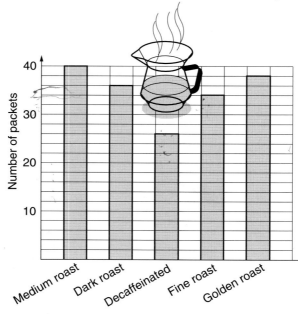

a Which type of coffee was most popular?
b How many more packets of fine roast were sold than decaffeinated?
c How many packets were sold altogether?
d The target for weekly sales was 200 packets.
   Did Kelly's reach their target?

3 Kelly's kept a record of their coffee sales over a ten-week period.
This line graph shows their figures.

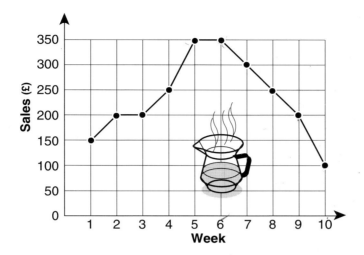

a For how many weeks were the sales more than £200?

b What were their sales in: (i) week 1 (ii) week 9?

c Their best sales were during the local jazz festival.
Which two weeks were these?

d How many more packets of coffee did they sell in week 6 than in week 10?

4 Kelly's also sells chocolates.
This pie chart shows the sales of their special gift packs.

Their best seller is *Belgian Dark.*

Their poorest seller is *Alpine White.*

One quarter of their sales is *Mixed Continental.*

The other kind they sell is *Swiss Soft Centre.*

A stands for *Belgian Dark.*

Make similar statements about B, C and D.

Bar Graphs

Ian did a survey of the colour of cars in a multi-storey car park.
He made a bar graph of his results.

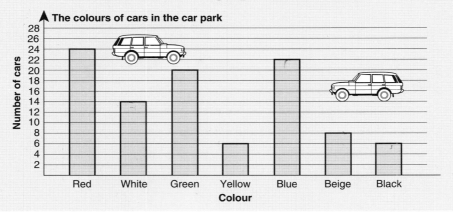

EXERCISE 1

1 Examine Ian's bar graph and answer the following questions.

   a Which was the most popular car colour?
   b What can you say about yellow and black cars?
   c How many green cars were there?
   d List the colours in order of popularity.
   e A sign at the car park read 'Parking for 100 cars'.
      How many car spaces were unused?

2 Mairi was at the Butterfly Farm.
She recorded the number of different butterflies she saw.
She put her results in a **horizontal** bar graph.

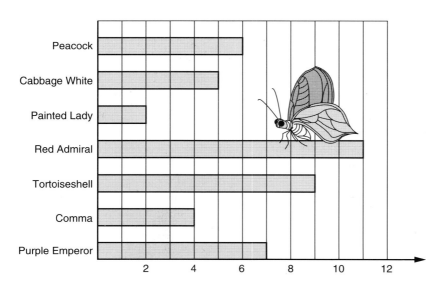

   a How many Tortoiseshell butterflies did Mairi see?

   b How many Red Admiral butterflies did she see?

   c What was the most common butterfly?

   d List the butterflies in order, with the most common first.

   e A fact-sheet said Comma was the fifth most common butterfly to be found. Was this true in Mairi's case?

3 This bar graph shows the temperatures around the world in degrees Celsius (°C).

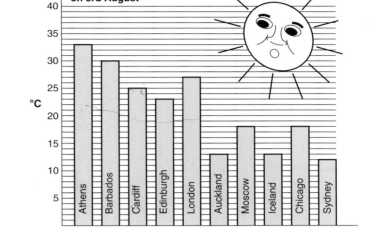

a Which is the hottest place recorded?

b Which places are warmer than 20 °C?

c What is the difference between the warmest and coldest place?

d The average temperature in Britain is 23 °C. How much hotter than this is Cardiff?

e How much warmer is it in London than in Auckland?

f How much cooler is it in Chicago than in Edinburgh?

g Which places are 5 degrees cooler than Moscow?

h A newspaper article said that London was the third hottest place recorded. Was this true?

4 This bar graph is in two parts.

CALDERVALE HIGH SCHOOL
TOWERS ROAD
AIRDRIE
ML6 8PG

British Butterflies

The size of the butterfly

7 cm 6 5 4 3 2 1 0 cm

How common it is

0 Rare Fairly rare Average Common Very common

Marbled White
Painted Lady
White Admiral
Purple Emperor
Common Blue
Small Copper

a Which is the largest butterfly?

b Which is the rarest butterfly?

c Which butterfly is very common in Britain?

d Which butterflies are common in Britain?

e Which butterflies are the same size?

f How many butterflies are more than 3 cm?

g Which butterfly is fairly rare?

h List the butterflies in order, largest first.

i List the butterflies in order, rarest first.

Do Worksheet 1

Line Graphs

A line graph is another good way to present information.
Newspapers, magazines and television often use this method.
This line graph shows the weight of a foal from birth to nine weeks.

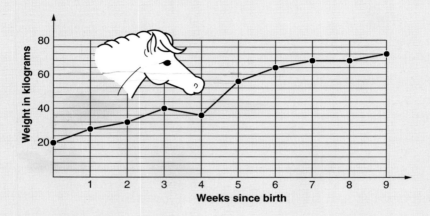

Notice that:
- every horizontal line means 4 kg
- in general the graph is rising. This is called the **trend**.

EXERCISE 2

1 **a** What weight was the foal when he was born?
   b How much weight had he put on by the end of week 1?
   c What weight was he at week 5?
   d What happened between weeks 3 and 4?
   e Between which two weeks did he gain most weight?
   f When did his weight not change?
   g What weight was the foal at the end of this nine-week period?
   h How much weight had he put on during this time?

2 Describe the trend in each of these line graphs.

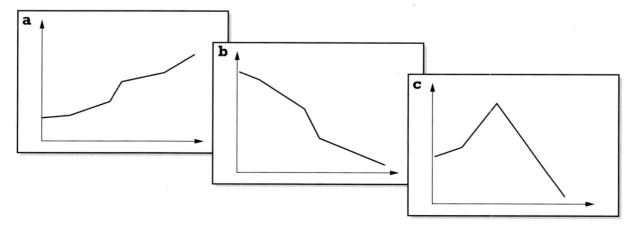

3 Zoe and her friend Zack cycle to Bickton and back.

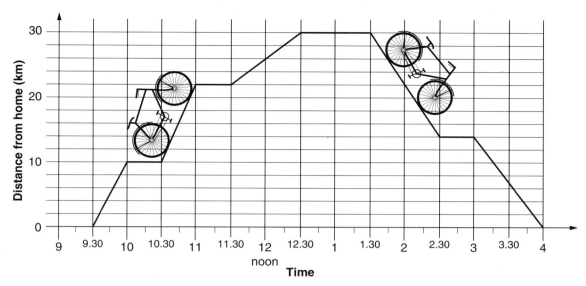

a At what time did they set off?
b How long was their first stop?
c How far from home were they at 11 am?
d They arrived at Bickton at 12.30. How far away from home is it?
e How long did they stay in Bickton?
f How far did they travel between 1.30 pm and 2.30 pm?
g How far did they travel on the last leg of the journey?

Do
Worksheet
2

4

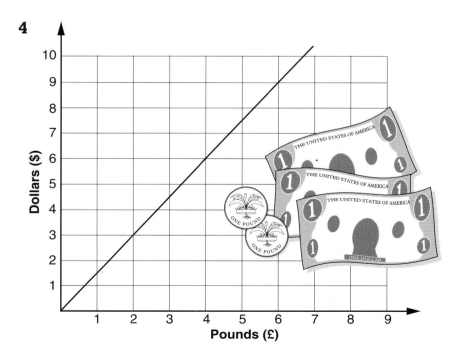

This graph lets you change pounds (£) into dollars($).

a How many dollars do you get for:
　(i) £2　　(ii) £6?

b How many dollars do you get for £1?

c How many pounds do you get for $6?

Line graphs are often used as ready reckoners.

5

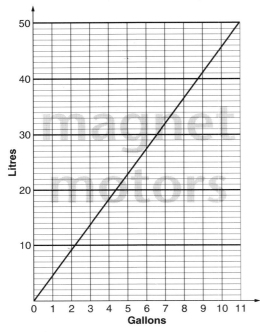

Magnet Motors give away
a free chart to convert gallons to litres.

a Roughly how many litres make:
(i) 2 gallons   (ii) 5 gallons   (iii) 8 gallons?

b Roughly how many gallons are in:
(i) 32 litres   (ii) 40 litres   (iii) 10 litres?

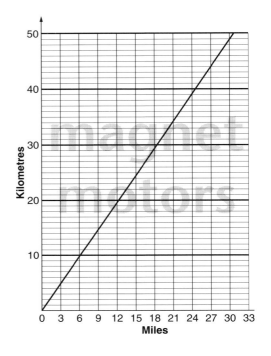

6 On the back of the chart is a ready
reckoner which changes miles
into kilometres.

a Roughly how many miles make:
(i) 20 km   (ii) 30 km   (iii) 50 km?

b Roughly how many kilometres are in:
(i) 15 miles   (ii) 21 miles   (iii) 27 miles?

7

This chart helps you change temperatures
from degrees Celsius (°C) to degrees
Fahrenheit (°F).

a Roughly how many °C make:
(i) 100 °F   (ii) 80 °F   (iii) 60 °F?

b Roughly how many °F make:
(i) 44 °C   (ii) 10 °C   (iii) 4 °C?

Pie Charts

Some people were asked
'What is your favourite take-away food?'
This pie chart shows the results.

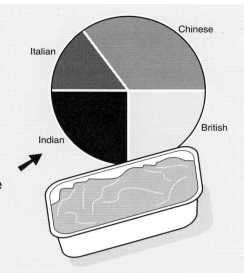

You can see that
one quarter of the people
chose an Indian meal.

EXERCISE 3

1 Use the pie chart to answer the questions.
   a What was the most popular choice?
   b What fraction chose British food?
   c What fraction of the people picked British or Indian?
   d One third chose Chinese. 60 people were asked.
      How many chose Chinese?
   e List the choices, with the most popular first.

2 Mr Methven's music class had 24 pupils.
They voted for their favourite musical instruments.
The pie chart shows how they voted.

Instrument	Number who voted
Violin	4
Drum	1
Guitar	8
Piano	5
Bass	6

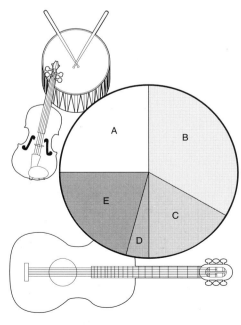

   a Look at the figures and decide which
      instrument is represented by:
      (i) B   (ii) D   (iii) E.
   b What fraction liked:
      (i) instrument A   (ii) instrument B?
   c What fraction liked either violin or guitar?

Average

'The average number in a bunch is 42.'

'Average rainfall is 2.5 cm.'

'The average temperature is 24 °C.'

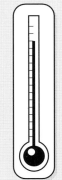

> The average (or mean) of a list of numbers is worked out by:
>
> **adding** the numbers together and then **dividing** by how many numbers are in the list.

Example Four boxes contain 46, 44, 42 and 40 matches. What is the average amount per box?

$$\text{Average or mean} = \frac{46 + 44 + 42 + 40}{4} = 43$$

EXERCISE 4

1

Coffee £2.54   Coffee £2.68   Coffee £2.46

Three jars of coffee were priced as shown. What is the average cost of a jar?

2 Eight pupils scored the following marks in their maths tests:
86%, 74%, 44%, 53%, 62%, 50%, 58% and 77%.
What was the average mark?

3

Joanna and her four friends weighed themselves. Here are their weights:
56 kg, 58.5 kg, 49.7 kg, 50.4 kg and 52.9 kg.
What was their average weight?

4 Mrs Thomson's phone bills for the four quarters of a year were:
£102.56, £78.32, £89.50 and £91.02.
What was her average phone bill?

5 The weights of eight men in a rugby pack were:
104 kg, 112 kg, 108.7 kg, 99.3 kg, 109 kg, 106.5 kg, 113 kg and 111.5 kg.
What was their average weight?

6 Over a ten-day period the following temperatures were recorded:
65 °F, 63 °F, 69 °F, 72 °F, 74 °F, 79 °F, 77 °F, 80 °F, 82 °F and 79 °F.
What was the average temperature?

CHECK-UP ON GRAPHS

1 Last week Mr Smith the French teacher gave his class a test.
He marked it out of 25.
The pass mark was 13.
The bar graph shows his pupils' marks.

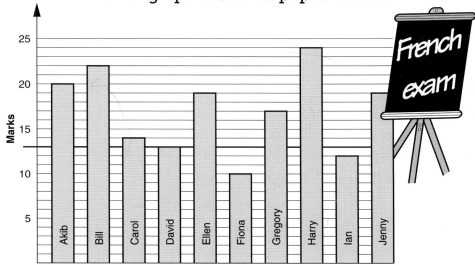

a Who was top of the class?
b Who was second?
c Who failed the test?
d Who was one mark short of a pass?

2

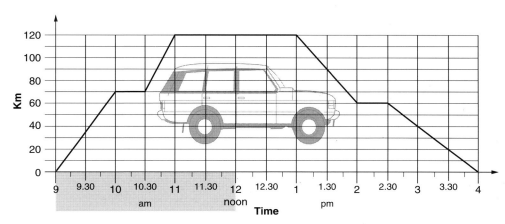

Ms Brown travelled from home to a business meeting 120 km away.
This is a line graph of her journey.

a How far was she from home when she stopped at a garage?
b How long did it take her once she left the garage to get to the meeting?
c What time did she arrive at the meeting?
d How long did the meeting last?
e On the way home she stopped at a café for a quick lunch.
What time was it?

3

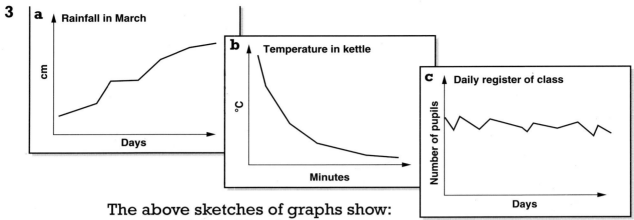

a Rainfall in March — cm / Days

b Temperature in kettle — °C / Minutes

c Daily register of class — Number of pupils / Days

The above sketches of graphs show:

a the rainfall in March

b the heat in a kettle when it is switched off

c the number of pupils registered each day in a class.

Describe the trend of each graph.

4 A supermarket issues a ready reckoner to help customers change from pounds to kilograms.

a Roughly how many kilograms make:
   (i)   1 pound
   (ii) 5 pounds
   (iii) 10 pounds?

b Roughly how many pounds make:
   (i) 1.8 kg (ii) 3.1 kg (iii) 4 kg?

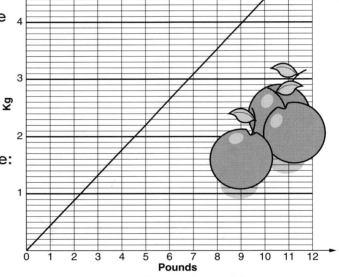

Kilograms to pounds — Kg / Pounds

5

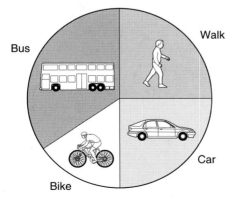

Bus, Walk, Bike, Car

This pie chart shows how 36 pupils came to school one day.

a What fraction walked?

b How many walked?

c What was:
   (i) the least popular way
   (ii) the most popular way to get to school?

6 Over a ten-day spell these temperatures were recorded:

17 °C, 19 °C, 22 °C, 24 °C, 27 °C, 25 °C, 19 °C, 20 °C, 24 °C and 23 °C.

What was the average daily temperature for this time?

11 2-D SHAPES

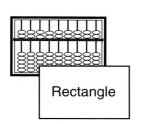
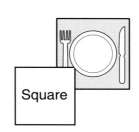

Rectangle   Square   Triangle   Circle

LOOKING BACK

1

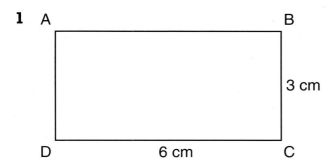

A _____ B

3 cm

D _____ 6 cm _____ C

a Copy this rectangle and mark on it the length of:
(i) AB   (ii) AD.
b What is the size of each angle in the rectangle?
c Put a small 'x' in ∠ABC.
d Make another copy of the rectangle. Use dotted lines to show the lines of symmetry.

A _____ B

5 cm

D _____ C

2 a Copy this square and mark on it the length of each side.
b What is the size of each angle in the square?
c Put a small 'x' in ∠ABC.
d Make another copy of the square. Use dotted lines to show the lines of symmetry.

3 Match each label with a letter.

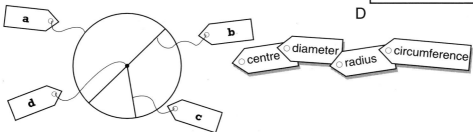

centre   diameter   radius   circumference

4 Work out the size of the missing angle.

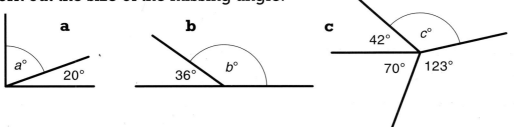

a $a°$ 20°

b 36° $b°$

c 42° $c°$ 70° 123°

111

| The angles of a triangle add up to 180°. |

Example   What is the size of the missing angle?

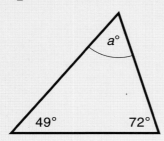

$49 + 72 = 121$

$180 - 121 = 59$

so $a° = 59°$

EXERCISE 1

1   Mr Thomson is an architect.
He draws plans.
Here are some roof spaces he has drawn.
Work out the missing angles.

a

44° $a°$ 41°

b

68°

35° $b°$

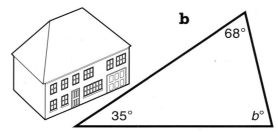

c

$c°$ $e°$

52°   90° $d°$ 28°

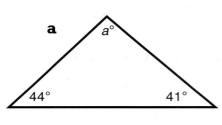

d

$g°$

120° $f°$ 80°

2   Here is a more complex roof space.

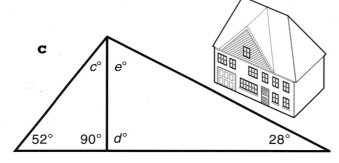

85° $s°$

$s°$ $r°$

42° $p°$ 90° $q°$ 50°

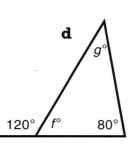

a Work out the size of:
  (i) $p°$ (ii) $q°$ (iii) $r°$.

b Both angles marked $s°$ are the same size.
What is the value of s?

3 The pennants on top of the castle are triangles.
  a What is the value of *x* in the first triangle?
  b The angles in a straight line make 180°.
    What is the value of (i) *a*   (ii) *b*?
  c Work out the values of *c, d* and *e*.

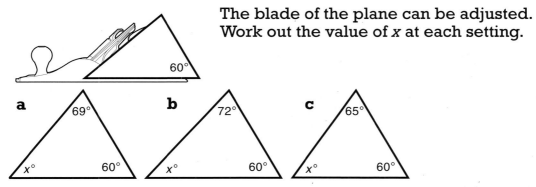

4

The diagram shows the sail and mast of a yacht.
  a Work out the size of *p*°.   **b** Calculate the value of *q*.

5 A company makes wire paperclips and wire coathangers.

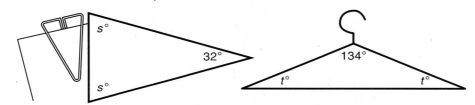

  a Both angles marked *s*° are the same size. What is the value of *s*?
  b Both angles marked *t*° are the same size. What is the value of *t*?

6   The blade of the plane can be adjusted.
                             Work out the value of *x* at each setting.

a 69° *x*° 60°

b 72° *x*° 60°

c 65° *x*° 60°

7 The piece of a sundial which casts the shadow is a triangle.
It always points north.
The angle marked *x* is the latitude of the place where the sundial is.
Work out the latitude of each sundial.

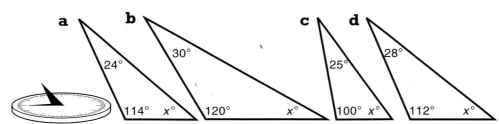

Some Special Triangles

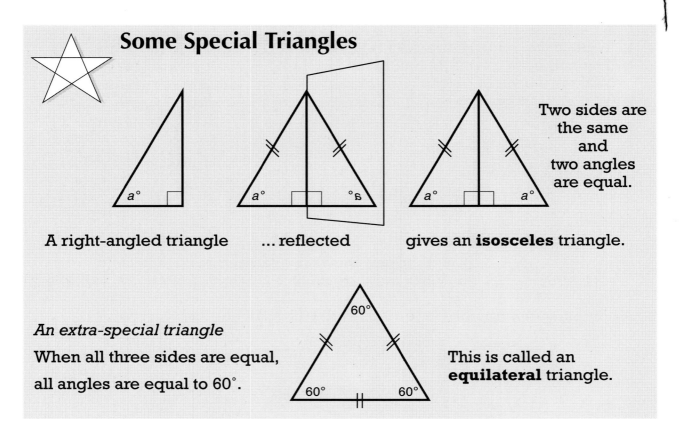

A right-angled triangle   ...reflected   gives an **isosceles** triangle.

Two sides are
the same
and
two angles
are equal.

An extra-special triangle

**When all three sides are equal,
all angles are equal to 60°.**

This is called an
equilateral triangle.

EXERCISE 2

1

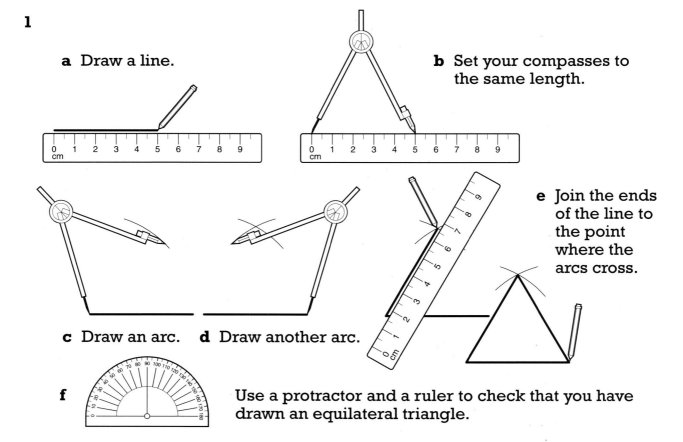

a Draw a line.

b Set your compasses to the same length.

c Draw an arc.   **d** Draw another arc.

e Join the ends of the line to the point where the arcs cross.

f Use a protractor and a ruler to check that you have drawn an equilateral triangle.

2 **a** Draw a line.

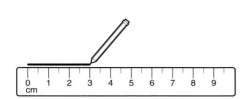

b Set your compasses **longer** than the line.

c Now draw arcs and form a triangle as in question **1**.

d Use a protractor and a ruler to check that you have drawn an isosceles triangle.

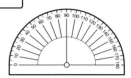

3 The sail is a right-angled triangle. What is the size of the angle marked $a°$?

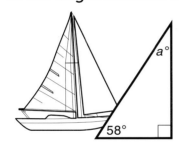

4 The outline of the tent is an equilateral triangle.

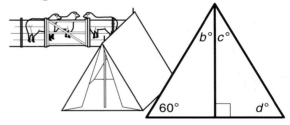

Calculate the size of the angle marked:
(i) $b°$ (ii) $c°$ (iii) $d°$.

5

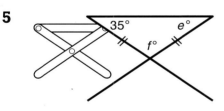

The camp stool forms an isosceles triangle. Work out the size of the angles marked $e°$ and $f°$.

6 All the sides of the snooker triangle are the same length. What is the size of each angle?

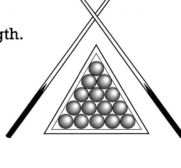

7 **a** How many isosceles triangles are in the outline of the garden gate?
  b How many equilateral triangles are in the outline of the garden gate?
  c Work out the size of the angle marked:
    (i) $g°$ (ii) $h°$ (iii) $j°$ (iv) $k°$.

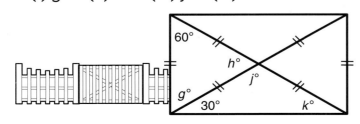

Do Worksheet **1**

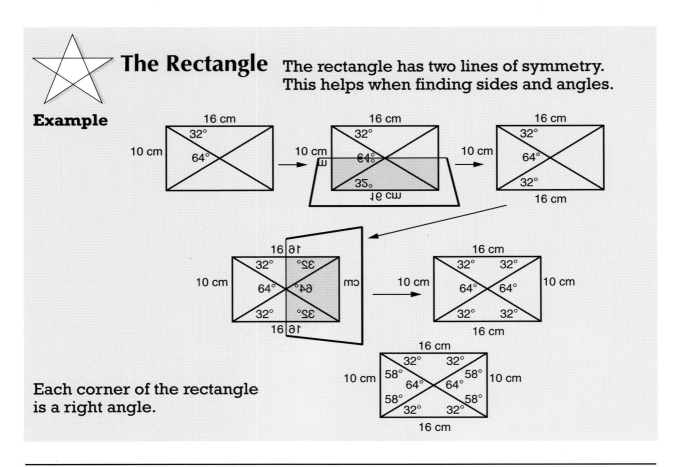

The Rectangle The rectangle has two lines of symmetry.
This helps when finding sides and angles.

Example

Each corner of the rectangle
is a right angle.

EXERCISE 3

1 (i) Copy each diagram.

(ii) Fill in the sizes of as many sides and angles as you can.

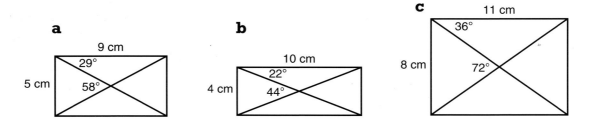

a 9 cm, 29°, 5 cm, 58°

b 10 cm, 22°, 4 cm, 44°

c 11 cm, 36°, 8 cm, 72°

2 a Use the lines of symmetry to help you find the value of:

(i) *a* cm   (ii) *b* cm   (iii) *c* cm.

b How long are the diagonals of the
rectangle?

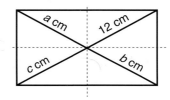

3 The doorway is a rectangle.
From A to C is 2 metres.
How far is it from B to D?

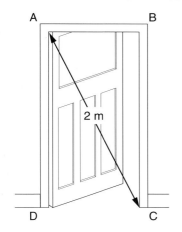

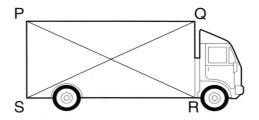

4 The side of the lorry is a rectangle.
From P to R is 8 metres.
What is the length from S to Q?

5 Farmer Brown has a field.
A plan of it is shown.
He would like to know the length of the
path from K to M.
However, there is a bull in the
enclosure.

  a What is the length of:
    (i) LM   (ii) MN?
  b What is the length of the path KM?

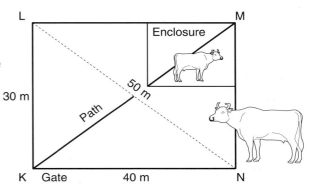

6

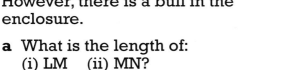

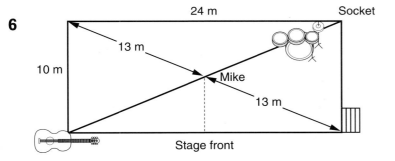

Jan is setting up the stage
for the concert.
She wants to know *quickly*
the distance from the mike
to the socket.
The drum kit is in the way.

  a What is the distance from the mike to the socket?
  b How far is it from the mike to the corner with the guitar?
  c How far is it from the mike to the front of the stage?

7 The drawbridge is 13 m long.
The moat is 5 m wide.
The end of the drawbridge is 12 m off the
ground.
How long must the invader's ladder be to reach
the wall as shown?

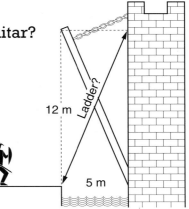

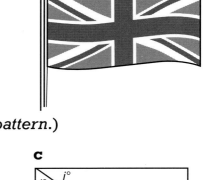

8 Jane has been drawing flags from all around the world.

(i) Make a sketch of each one.
(ii) Fill in the lengths of the missing sides.
(iii) Work out the values of the angles marked.
(The dashed lines are symmetry lines in the *pattern*.)

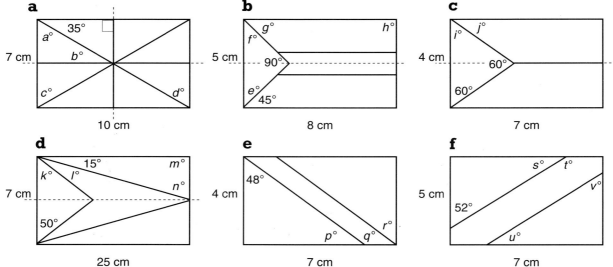

(Hint: these flags look the same upside-down.)

A Special Rectangle: The Square

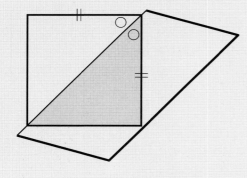

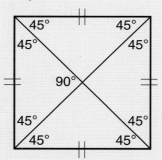

The square has two more lines of symmetry.
All four sides are the same.
The right angles are cut in half by the diagonals.
The diagonals cross at right angles.

EXERCISE 4

1

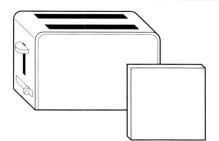

Peter has cut himself a square piece of bread. How many different ways can he drop it into the toaster?
(Only consider one slot.)

2 A domino is made from two squares.

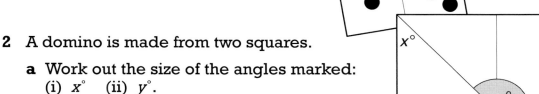

  a Work out the size of the angles marked:
    (i) $x°$ (ii) $y°$.

  b How long is the domino?

3 cm

z cm

3

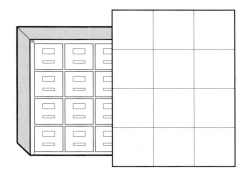

The filing cabinet has 12 drawers.
The front of each drawer is a square.
The height of a drawer is 40 cm.

  a How high is the cabinet?

  b How wide is the cabinet?

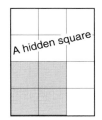

A hidden square

  c How many squares can you find in the drawing? (One possible square is shown shaded.)

4 We often make use of an important property of the square. It tiles.
A manufacturer sells tiles which contain letters of the alphabet.
Each tile is 12 cm long.

  a The name ANNE has been spelt out in tiles.
    How long is the name?

ANNE

  b How long will each of the following names be?
    (i) JOE   (ii) JENNY   (iii) MICHAEL   (iv) ELIZABETH

  c How many letters are in a name whose length is:
    (i) 24 cm   (ii) 72 cm   (iii) 96 cm?

5 A decorative floor tile has sides 15 cm long.

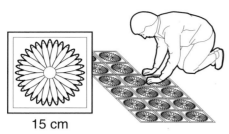

15 cm

A workman wants to tile an area with these tiles.
The area is 300 cm long by 150 cm wide.

a How many tiles will he need for a 300 cm row?
b How many rows will he need?
c How many tiles will he need for the area?

6 A shop sells packets of novelty tiles.
They tile similar to the way bricks fit in a wall.

a Cut out the cat tiles on Worksheet 2.
Glue them into your jotter to show how
they tile.
b Cut out the dog tiles and see if you can
make them tile.

7 Many shapes tile. Rectangles and triangles are two examples.
Make a collection of pictures from magazines which show examples of tiling.

8 Use tracing paper to explore how these shapes tile.

a

3 sides

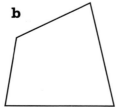

b

4 sides

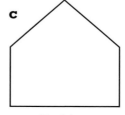

c

5 sides

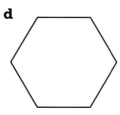

d

6 sides

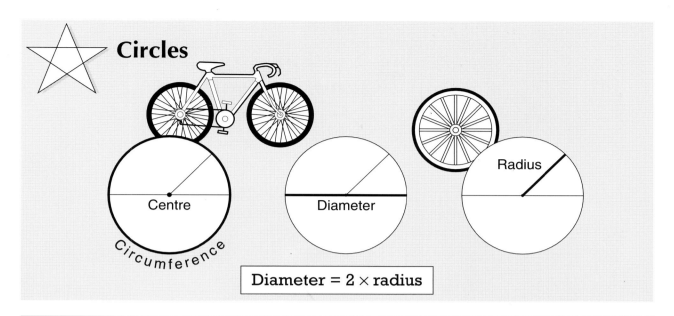

Circles

Diameter = 2 × radius

EXERCISE 5

1 Work out the diameter of each circle.

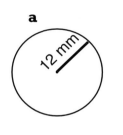

a 12 mm

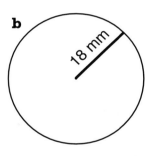

b 18 mm

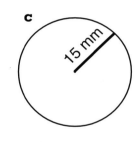

c 15 mm

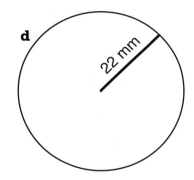

d 22 mm

2 Work out the radius of each coin.

a 20 mm

b 17 mm

c 26 mm

d 24 mm

e 22 mm

3

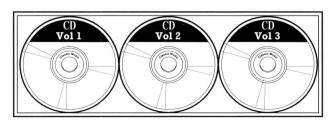

Three CDs fit in a presentation box. The diameter of each disc is 12 cm.

Work out:
a the length of the box
b the breadth of the box.

4 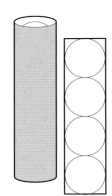 Four ping-pong balls are packed in a tube.
From the side they look like four circles in a rectangle.
The radius of each circle is 3 cm.

   a What is the diameter of one circle?

   b What is the height of the rectangle?

   c What is the width of the rectangle?

5 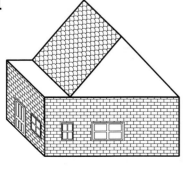 Cans of beans are packed in boxes of six.
From above the box looks like this:

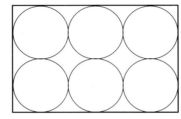

The diameter of each can is 7 cm.

   a What is the length of the box?
   b What is the breadth of the box?

6 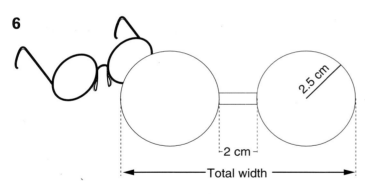 These sun-shades clip onto glasses.
The radius of each lens is 2.5 cm.
The lenses are 2 cm apart.
Work out the total
width of the shades.

Do Worksheet 3

CHECK-UP ON 2-D SHAPES

1 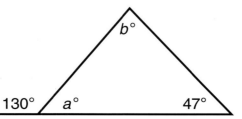 The roof space of the doll's house is as shown.
Work out the value of:
  a *a*   **b** *b*.

2

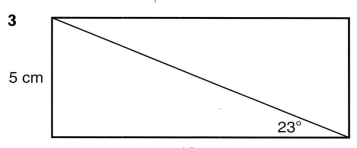

The dashed line is a line of symmetry of the triangle.

a What is the size of the angle marked:
(i) $p°$ (ii) $q°$?

b Work out the size of the angle marked:
(i) $r°$ (ii) $s°$.

3

5 cm

23°

12 cm

a Make a sketch of this rectangle.
b Mark the length of each side.
c Mark the size of each angle.

4

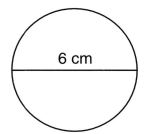

The side of the biscuit tin is made from two squares. The height of the tin is 8 cm.

a How long is the side of the tin?
b What is the size of the angle marked $x°$?

$x°$

8 cm

◄─────── Length ───────►

5 **a** What is the radius of this circle?   **b** What is the diameter of this circle?

6 cm

4 cm

6 Jani has made a present by boxing five £1 coins. The radius of one coin is 11 mm.

Work out:
a the diameter of a coin
b the breadth of the box
c the length of the box.

12 MEASUREMENT

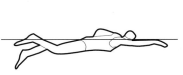

John swam 200 metres. The pencil is 8 **centi**metres long. The coin is 17 **milli**metres across. Megan has driven 145 **kilo**metres today.

LOOKING BACK

1 Choose the best units for measuring these:
  a the distance to London
  b the length of a football pitch
  c the width of a stamp
  d the thickness of a textbook
  e the height of a ceiling
  f the length of a journey
  g your waist measurement.

Millimetres   Centimetres

Metres   Kilometres

2 a Estimate the length of each line in **centimetres**.
  (i)
  (ii) _____
  (iii) _____
  b Measure the lines and check your estimates.

3 a Draw a rectangle 12 cm by 5 cm.
  b Draw in one diagonal.
  c Measure the diagonal in centimetres.

  You should get 13 centimetres.

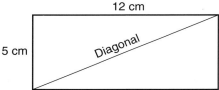

4 Write these lengths in **metres**. Example: 147 cm = 1.47 m.
  a 123 cm   **b** 256 cm   **c** 182 cm

5 Write these lengths in **centimetres**. Example: 1.31 m = 131 cm.
  a 1.52 m   **b** 4.63 m   **c** 2.08 m

6 List these people in order of height. Put the tallest first.

| Adam | Beth | Carol | David | Emma | Fraser | Grant |
| 1.62 m | 2.02 m | 1.59 m | 2.36 m | 1.02 m | 1.46 m | 1.12 m |

Using Millimetres

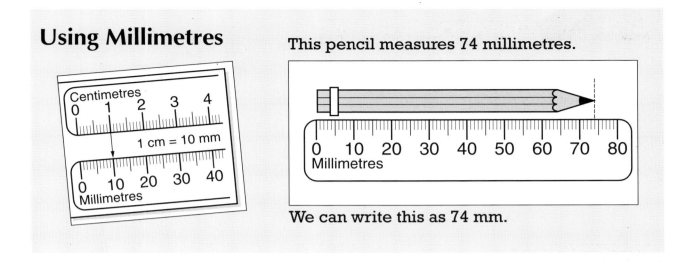

This pencil measures 74 millimetres.

We can write this as 74 mm.

EXERCISE 1

1 Write down the length of each pencil in millimetres.

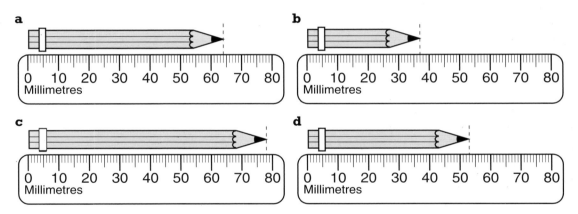

2 Write down the length of each object in millimetres.

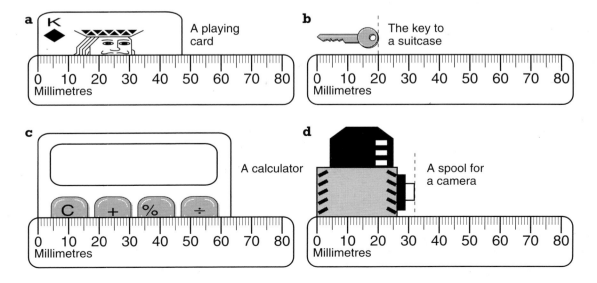

a   A playing card

b   The key to a suitcase

c   A calculator

d   A spool for a camera

3 Some of Mike's models are shown below.

First estimate the length or height of each.
Then measure each drawing in millimetres.

Make a table like the one opposite to record your results.

Object	Estimate	Actual measurement
a Car		
b Robot		
c Tree		
d Castle		
e Plane		

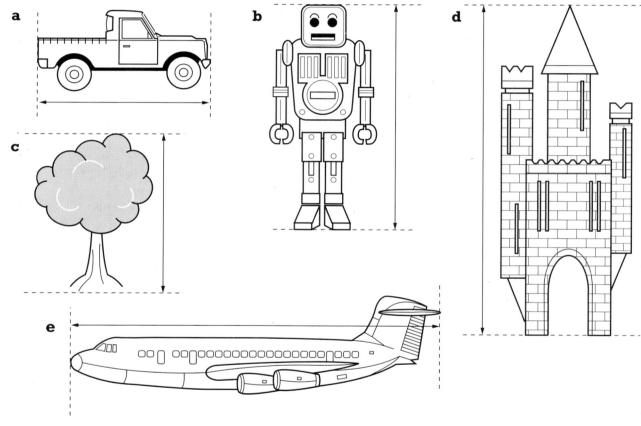

4 The Snail Derby

a Estimate the length of each snail trail in millimetres.

b Measure each length.

c List the trails in order. Begin with the longest.

(i) _____

(ii) _____

(iii) _____

(iv) _____

(v) _____

5 **a** Estimate the height and width of each flag in millimetres.
   b Measure each height and width in millimetres.

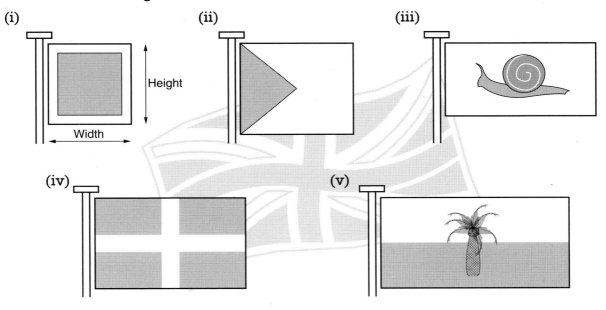

(i) Height Width (ii) (iii)

(iv) (v)

6 Stephen is a stamp designer.
He is making Christmas stamps.
He has the choice of various rectangles to use:

   a 30 mm by 40 mm (see opposite)
   b 35 mm by 35 mm
   c 40 mm by 25 mm.

Make an accurate drawing of each rectangle.

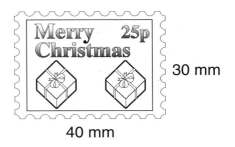

Merry Christmas 25p

30 mm

40 mm

7 Freda made sketches of some scraps of cloth she had.
All the angles were right angles.

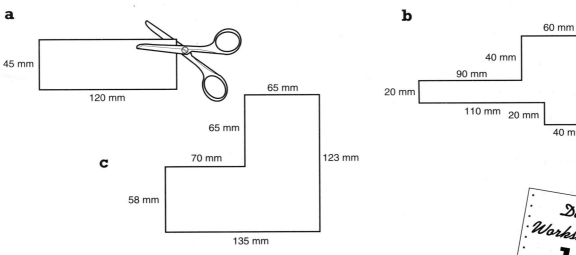

a

45 mm
120 mm

65 mm
65 mm
70 mm
123 mm

c

58 mm
135 mm

b

60 mm
40 mm
90 mm
20 mm
80 mm
110 mm   20 mm
40 mm

Use a ruler and a protractor to
help you make accurate
drawings of the pieces of cloth.

Do Worksheet 1

Changing

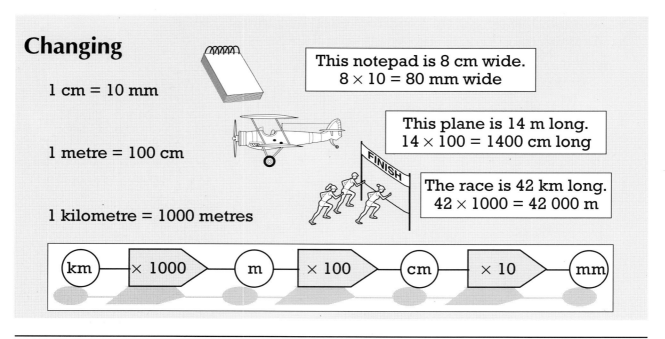

1 cm = 10 mm

This notepad is 8 cm wide.
$8 \times 10 = 80$ mm wide

1 metre = 100 cm

This plane is 14 m long.
$14 \times 100 = 1400$ cm long

1 kilometre = 1000 metres

The race is 42 km long.
$42 \times 1000 = 42\,000$ m

km — ×1000 — m — ×100 — cm — ×10 — mm

EXERCISE 2

1 Change these measurements to millimetres by multiplying by 10.
 a 2 cm **b** 5.3 cm **c** 1.9 cm **d** 13.3 cm **e** 11.6 cm

2 Change these measurements to centimetres by multiplying by 100.
 a 38 m **b** 4 m **c** 2.6 m **d** 18 m **e** 1.2 m

3 Change these measurements to metres by multiplying by 1000.
 a 2 km **b** 3.5 km **c** 12 km **d** 1.75 km **e** 0.6 km

4 Some pupils in a class listed how far they
 lived from school.

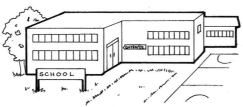

Alan 1200 m
Bryan 1045 m
Colin 1.3 km
Danielle 1.02 km
Ellen 1.25 km

 a Change the kilometre distances to metres.
 b List the pupils in order. Put the pupil closest to school first.

5

bigger
than >

less than <

equals =

Write out each pair of measurements using the
correct sign: 'bigger than' or 'less than' or
'is equal to'.

 a 12 mm 1.2 cm **b** 36 mm 3.2 cm
 c 4.5 cm 42 mm **d** 2.8 m 250 cm
 e 640 m 0.64 km **f** 15.3 cm 152 mm

Changing Back

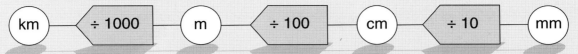

km — ÷ 1000 — m — ÷ 100 — cm — ÷ 10 — mm

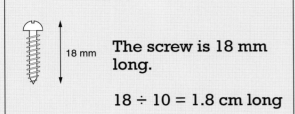

18 mm

The screw is 18 mm long.

$18 \div 10 = 1.8$ cm long

Graeme's putt was 320 cm long.

$320 \div 100 = 3.2$ m long

In 1991 Arturo Barrios ran 21 100 m in one hour.

$21\ 100 \div 1000 = 21.1$ km in one hour

EXERCISE 2B

1 Change the following to kilometres.
  a 1200 m   **b** 23 000 m **c** 560 m   **d** 300 m   **e** 75 100 m

2 Change the following to metres.
  a 120 cm   **b** 1300 cm **c** 740 cm   **d** 80 cm   **e** 15 000 cm

3 Change the following to centimetres.
  a 130 mm   **b** 20 mm **c** 620 mm **d** 80 mm   **e** 1190 mm

4 Gemma and George measured the heights of nine kittens:

Amy 123 mm   Bounce 109 mm   Chops 12.6 cm
Dimple 111 mm   Edna 13.4 cm   Fuzzy 138 mm
Grin 125 mm   Huggy 11.9 cm   Iggy 13.3 cm

  a Change the millimetre measurements to centimetres.
  b List the kittens with the tallest first.

5

The heights of some houses in a street were measured.

No. 1 7.25 m   No. 2 727 cm   No. 3 719 cm
No. 4 726 cm   No. 5 7.16 m   No. 6 709 cm

  a Change the centimetre measurements to metres.
  b List the houses, tallest first.

Do Worksheet **2**

6 Kirsty moved to Leeds. She noted the distances to various places.

Manchester 64 373 m   Birmingham 128 447 m   Kendal 115 473 m
Lincoln 136 394 m   Nottingham 104 407 m   Preston 90 123 m

  a Change each distance into kilometres. Ignore the figures after the point.
  b List the towns, putting the one closest to Leeds first.

Perimeter

The **perimeter** of a shape is the distance round the outside of the shape.

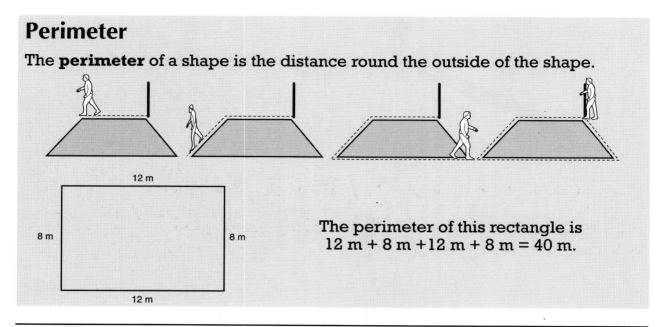

The perimeter of this rectangle is
12 m + 8 m + 12 m + 8 m = 40 m.

EXERCISE 3

1 Calculate the perimeters of these shapes by adding up the lengths of the sides.

a

5 cm

5 cm Square 5 cm

5 cm

b

6 cm

3 cm Rectangle 3 cm

6 cm

c

8 cm 10 cm

Right-angled triangle

6 cm

d

7 cm 7 cm

Equilateral triangle

7 cm

e

6 cm

6 cm 6 cm

Hexagon

6 cm 6 cm

6 cm

f

4 cm 4 cm

Rhombus

4 cm 4 cm

2 a Calculate the perimeter of the house and the garage together.

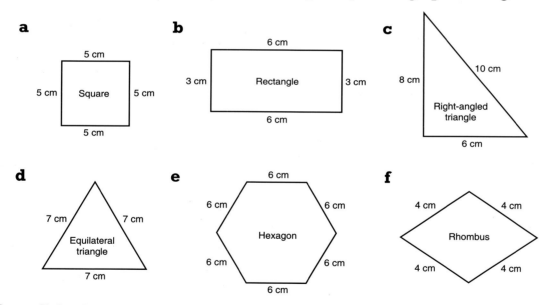

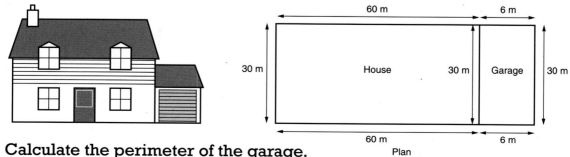

Plan

b Calculate the perimeter of the garage.
c Calculate the perimeter of the house.

3 Calculate the perimeters of these shapes.

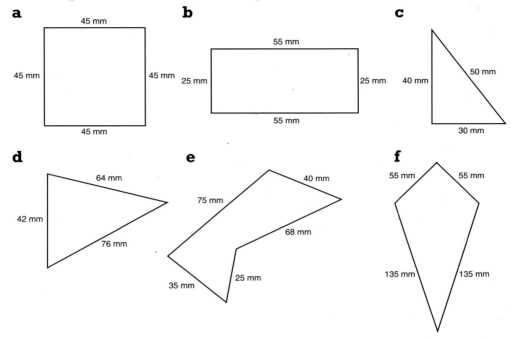

a
45 mm
45 mm 45 mm
45 mm

b
55 mm
25 mm 25 mm
55 mm

c
40 mm 50 mm
30 mm

d
64 mm
42 mm
76 mm

e
40 mm
75 mm
68 mm
35 mm 25 mm

f
55 mm 55 mm
135 mm 135 mm

4 Now change the perimeters of the shapes in question **3** to centimetres.

5 Kenneth has a model farm. He is fencing off some oddly shaped fields. Measure each shape and work out its perimeter in millimetres.

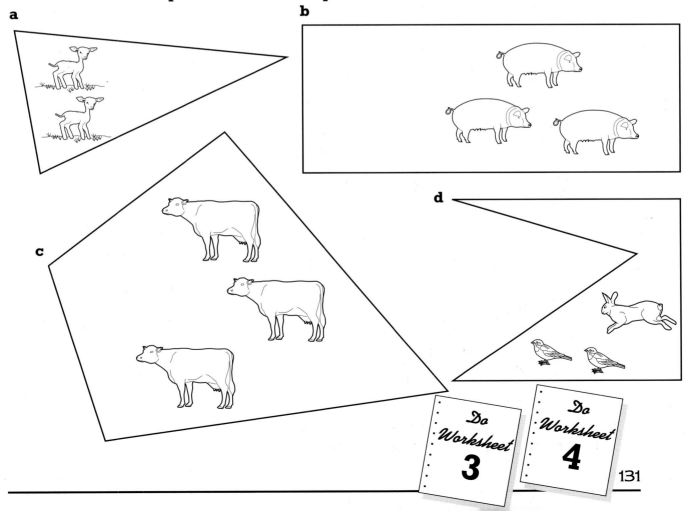

a

b

c

d

Do Worksheet **3**

Do Worksheet **4**

The cost of wallpapering a room depends on its perimeter.

Vince can measure each wall except where the Christmas tree is. Here is a plan of the room:

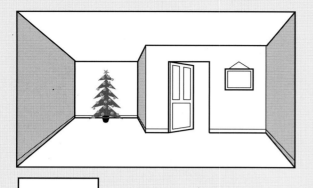

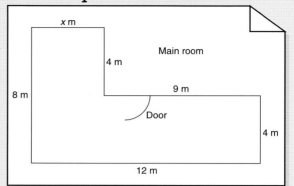

We can find the missing measurement by using measurements which are given.

$$3 \text{ m} + 9 \text{ m} = 12 \text{ m}$$

So the missing side is 3 m long.

EXERCISE 4

1 For each room, find:
  (i)   the missing measurement
  (ii) the perimeter.

a
Room 1
20 m
10 m
5 m
15 m
5 m
a

b
16 m
Room 2
5 m
5 m
12 m
10 m
5 m
b

c
12 m
Room 3
11 m
6 m
5 m
c
8 m

d
d
25 m
e
15 m
Room 4
10 m
22.5 m

e
12 m
6 m
6 m
12 m
Room 5
f
18 m

2 This is a plan of a school.

  a For each building:
    (i) work out the length of any missing sides
    (ii) calculate the perimeter.

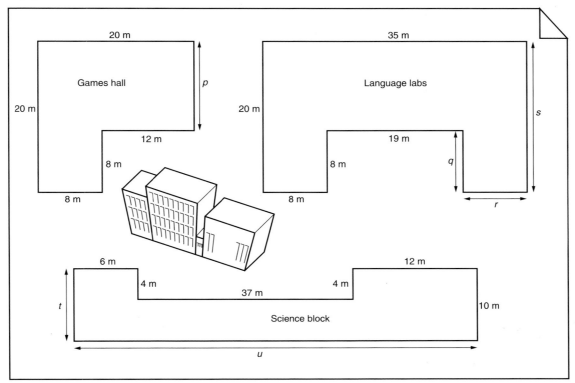

  b Which building has the largest perimeter?
  c Which building has the smallest perimeter?
  d The cost of fixing guttering depends on the total of all the perimeters. What is this total?

A Special Perimeter

The perimeter of a circle is given a special name. It is called the **circumference**.

The circumference of a circle is roughly **three times the diameter**.

Diameter ——[× 3]—— Circumference

Example

Diameter × 3
$6 \times 3 = 18$
Circumference ≈ 18 cm

The circumference of this circle is *about* 18 cm.

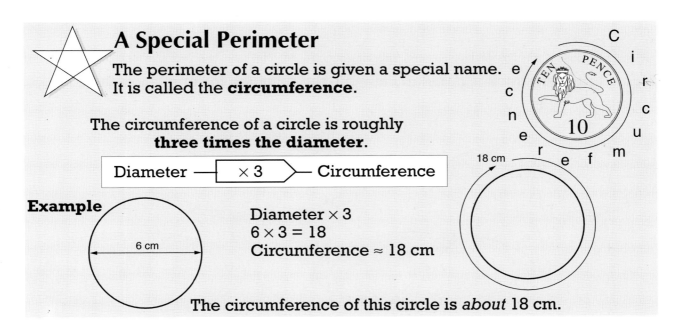

EXERCISE 5

1 Estimate the circumferences of these circles.

a

5 cm

b

4 cm

c

6 cm

d

85 mm

e

42 mm

f

35 mm

2 A coin has pencil lead scraped on its rim.

24 mm

When the coin rolls once it leaves a trail the size of its circumference.

≈ 72 mm

How long a trail will each coin leave?

a

2 cm

b

1.7 cm

c

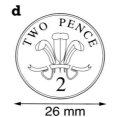

22 mm

d

26 mm

3 Each running track is circular. Estimate the distance for one lap of the track.

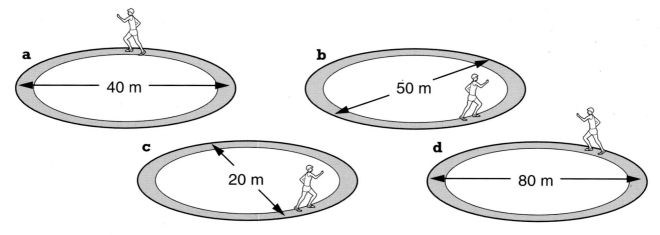

a 40 m

b 50 m

c 20 m

d 80 m

CHECK-UP ON MEASUREMENT

1 Measure the length of each model instrument in:
(i) millimetres   (ii) centimetres.

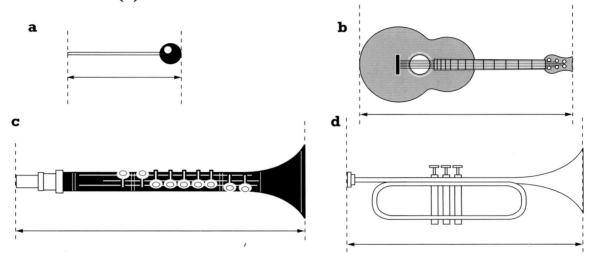

a

b

c

d

2 a Draw a rectangle 86 mm long and 52 mm wide.
b Draw a square of side 6 cm.

3 Change:
a 13 cm to mm	**b** 2.3 cm to mm	**c** 5 m to cm
d 4.2 m to cm	**e** 5 km to m	**f** 2.3 km to m
g 0.4 cm to mm	**h** 0.5 m to cm	**i** 0.5 km to m

4 Change:
a 30 mm to cm	**b** 25 mm to cm	**c** 600 cm to m
d 560 cm to m	**e** 7000 m to km	**f** 3400 m to km
g 6 mm to cm	**h** 40 cm to m	**i** 200 m to km

5 Bruce measured the lengths of some pens.
a Change all the cm lengths to mm.
b Put the lengths in order with the shortest first.

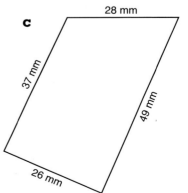

56 mm	116 mm
82 mm	11.5 cm
10.9 cm	6.6 cm
107 mm	10.3 cm
8.5 cm	102 mm

6 Calculate the perimeters of these shapes.

a

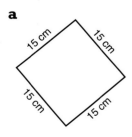

15 cm   15 cm   15 cm   15 cm

b

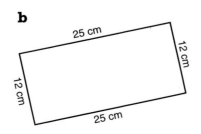

25 cm   12 cm   12 cm   25 cm

c

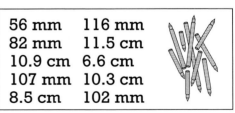

28 mm   37 mm   49 mm   26 mm

13 STATISTICS AND PROBABILITY

LOOKING BACK

1 Put this list of numbers in order, smallest first: 7.9, 7.09, 6.85, 6.9, 6, 7, 8.

2 Jack noted his petrol bill over six months: £20, £18, £30, £42, £40, £36. What is his average bill?

3 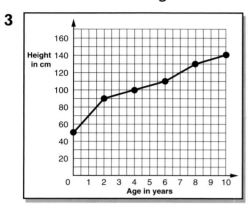 This chart shows Tim's height from when he was born until his tenth birthday.

    a What was his height at birth?
    b What was his height at:
       (i) 2 years   (ii) 4 years?
    c How much did he grow between ages 2 and 4?
    d His height wasn't recorded at 1 year. Use the graph to estimate it.

4 How likely is it that the following things will happen?
(Use these words: certain – very likely – evens – less than even – impossible.)

    a The sun will rise tomorrow.
    b A coin will land heads up.
    c The card at the top of a pack will be higher than 2.
    d You roll a dice and score 5.
    e You will see a live Stegosaurus when you visit the zoo.

Graphs

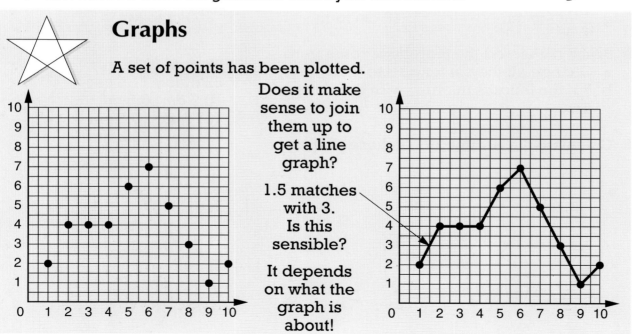

A set of points has been plotted. Does it make sense to join them up to get a line graph?

1.5 matches with 3. Is this sensible?

It depends on what the graph is about!

EXERCISE 1

1

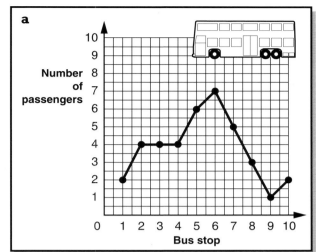

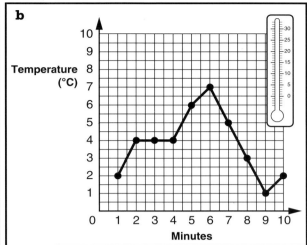

The graph shows the number of people on a bus at various stops.

How many passengers were on the bus halfway between stops 1 and 2? **Not 3!**

> You can't get stops between stop 1 and stop 2.

The sun came out for a minute or two. The temperature rose and fell.

Can you guess the temperature at 1.5 minutes?

> You can get times between 1 minute and 2 minutes.

2 a 3 people went to the cinema.
It cost £6.
4 people went to the cinema.
It cost £8.
Is it sensible to think about 3.2 people?

    b 3 litres of water weigh 3 kg.
4 litres of water weigh 4 kg.
Is it sensible to think about 3.2 litres?

    c 5 twenty pence coins are worth £1.
6 twenty pence coins are worth £1.20.
Is it sensible to think about 5.4 coins?

    d Mary weighed 28 kg at the age of 10.
She weighed 29 kg at the age of 11.
Is it sensible to think about 28.4 kg?

3 Which of the following do you think are sensible things to consider?

a 3.5 children	**b** 3.5 seconds	**c** 2.3 eggs
d 2.3 g	**e** 7.9 °C	**f** 7.2 footballs
g 8.3 shirts	**h** 4.6 litres	**i** 8.7 bicycles
j 9.2 cm	**k** 4.2 phonecalls	**l** a phonecall lasting 4.2 minutes

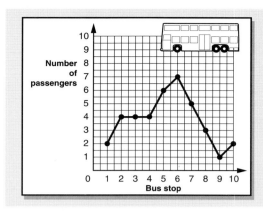

We can join the dots to highlight the trend ...

'The number of passengers rose until stop 6, then fell steadily until stop 9.'

... but we should be careful about whether readings between the points are sensible.

EXERCISE 2

1 In each graph:
   (i)   describe the trend
   (ii) say whether reading between the points is sensible or not.

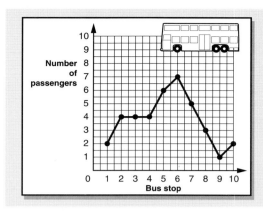

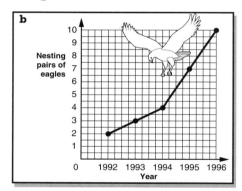

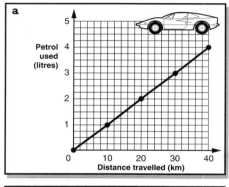

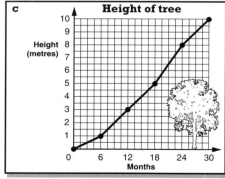

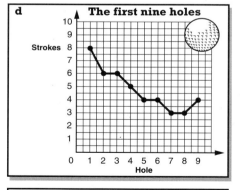

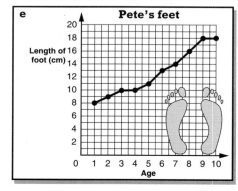

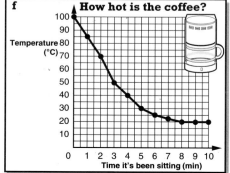

Averages: The Mean

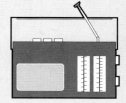

Kevin noted how long five programmes on the radio lasted:
35 minutes, 40 minutes, 42 minutes, 26 minutes, 42 minutes.
The mean length of a programme is:

$$\frac{35 + 40 + 42 + 26 + 42}{5} = 185 \div 5 = 37 \text{ minutes.}$$

> The **mean** is
> the total of the numbers
> divided by
> how many numbers there are.

EXERCISE 3

1

Stacey recorded some programmes.
Their lengths were:
20 minutes, 35 minutes, 30 minutes, 40 minutes, 45 minutes,
40 minutes.

a How many programmes did she record?
b What was the total time recorded?
c What was the mean length of a programme?

2 Some people drove to a meeting.
They each listed the distance they had travelled.
100 km, 70 km, 35 km, 40 km, 72 km.

a How many attended the meeting?
b What was the total distance covered?
c What was the mean distance covered?

3

Some boys at a club were asked their age.
Their answers were:
17 years, 16 years, 15 years, 16 years, 14 years,
15 years, 12 years.

a How many were asked? **b** What is the mean age?
c A new boy arrives. He is 16.
Is he older or younger than average?

4 Every day for two weeks Jan counted the wasps that
came into the classroom.
Her results were:
Mon 7, Tue 4, Wed 8, Thu 3, Fri 5, Mon 6, Tue 5, Wed 3, Thu 4, Fri 5.

a What was the mean number of wasps?
b She thought it unusual whenever there were more than 2 over the average.
Were there any unusual days?

Remember the Likelihood Line

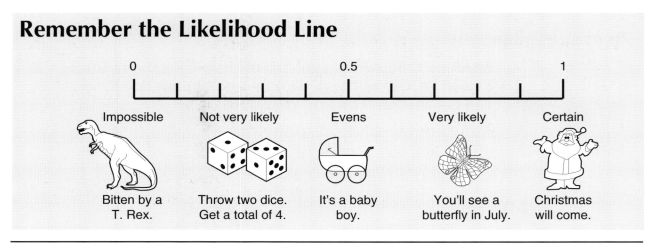

Impossible	Not very likely	Evens	Very likely	Certain
Bitten by a T. Rex.	Throw two dice. Get a total of 4.	It's a baby boy.	You'll see a butterfly in July.	Christmas will come.

EXERCISE 4

1 None of the following is actually impossible.
Each pair contains one thing more likely than the other.
Name the more likely event.

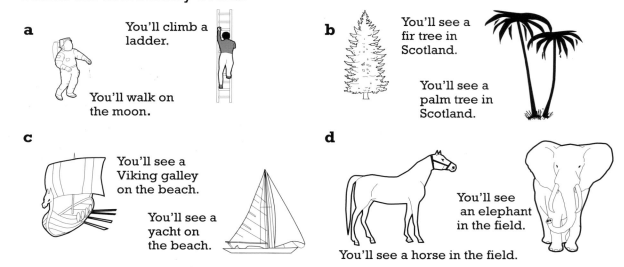

a You'll climb a ladder.

You'll walk on the moon.

b You'll see a fir tree in Scotland.

You'll see a palm tree in Scotland.

c You'll see a Viking galley on the beach.

You'll see a yacht on the beach.

d You'll see an elephant in the field.

You'll see a horse in the field.

2 Bill and Ted play with a dice.
Bill wins when it's less than 3. Ted wins when it is 3 or more.
  a List the ways that: (i) Bill can win (ii) Ted can win.
  b List the things that can happen.
  c Who is more likely to win?

3 There are five mugs in a row.
Some of them contain a pea.
Jill wins if she picks a mug with a pea.
  a How many ways can Jill: (i) win (ii) lose?
  b Which is more likely?

4 One hand holds the prize. Guess right and it's yours.
  a How many ways can you: (i) win (ii) lose?
  b Comment on which is more likely

Placing a Number on the Likelihood Line

Eight numbered balls go in a bag.
Zoe must pick the 3 or 4 to win.

There are only two ways of winning out of eight.

We say the likelihood, or probability, of winning is 0.25.

$$\frac{2}{8} = 2 \div 8 = 0.25$$

Place it on the likelihood line.
See where it is in relation to impossible and certain.

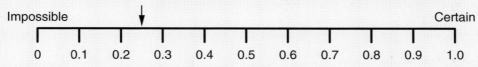

Impossible   Certain

| 0 | 0.1 | 0.2 | 0.3 | 0.4 | 0.5 | 0.6 | 0.7 | 0.8 | 0.9 | 1.0 |

EXERCISE 5

1 Freda is going to pick from these cards.
If she picks an even number she wins.
a How many winning cards are there?
b How many cards are there altogether?
c Freda will win two times out of five.
Write the likelihood of her winning as a decimal.
d Draw a likelihood line and point out Freda's chances.

2 A greengrocer sets up a sign like this:

T O M A T O E S

One of the letters falls over.
Work out the likelihood, as a decimal, of it being:

a T   **b** O   **c** M   **d** M, A or T.

3 Grant has 12 coins in his pocket.
He pulls one out at random.
What is the probability that it is:
a copper coloured
b round
c more than 10p
d 2p?

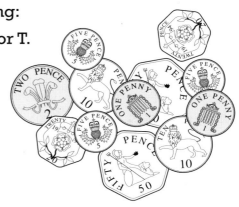

4 Here is a picture of the planets in the solar system.

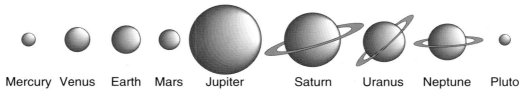

Mercury Venus Earth Mars Jupiter Saturn Uranus Neptune Pluto

a How many planets are there?
b How many have rings?
c If one is picked at random, what is the probability it will have:
  (i) rings
  (ii) intelligent life?

5

| | Miss a turn | Safe | Miss a turn | Safe | Miss a turn | Home |

It is Dave's throw.
He is travelling in the direction of the arrow.
What is the probability that he will:
a land on a 'Miss a turn'
b land on a safe square
c get home?

6 Ben goes to an art gallery.
He sees paintings by different artists:
4 by Degas, 3 by van Gogh, 1 by Munch, 2 by Rembrandt and 2 by Dali.
He picks one at random to study.
What is the probability it is:
a by Degas
b by van Gogh
c not by Dali?

7 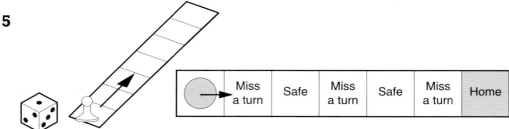 A pack of cards contains 52 cards.
There are four jacks, four queens and four kings.
These are called the face cards.
What is the probability that a card picked at random will be:
a a face card
b a queen
c a jack or a king?

CHECK-UP ON STATISTICS AND PROBABILITY

1

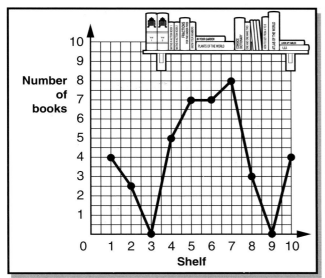

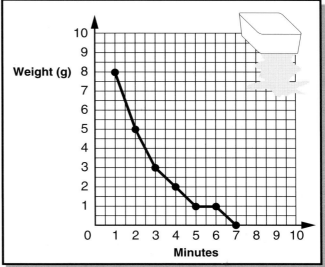

This graph shows the number of books on each shelf in a class.

This graph shows the weight of the ice left as an ice cube melts.

a Is it sensible to consider:

    (i) the 2.5th shelf   (ii) 2.5 books   (iii) 2.5 minutes   (iv) 2.5 g?

b Answer the sensible questions.
    (i)   How many books are on the 4.5th shelf?
    (ii) Which shelf holds 5.6 books?
    (iii) Which shelves hold more than 5.6 books?
    (iv) What is the weight of the cube after 3.5 minutes?
    (v) When did the cube weigh 6.5 g?

2  The heights of the books are:
16 cm, 18 cm, 15 cm, 14 cm, 17 cm, 16 cm.
Calculate the mean height.

3 There are ten houses in a street.
They are numbered 1 to 10.
One is selected at random for a visit
by a TV company.
What is the probability that:
a it is even numbered
b the number is greater than 3
c it is number 12?

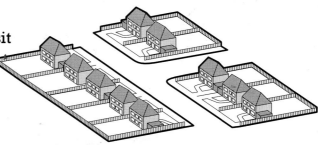

14 ALGEBRA

Reminder

There are 3 five pence coins and
4 twenty pence coins.
We can write this in a shorter way like this:
$3f + 4t.$

LOOKING BACK

1 Work out the missing number.

a
IN
(12) — −5 > OUT (?)

b
IN
(?) — −4 > OUT (12)

c
IN
(?) — +9 > OUT (13)

d
IN
(11) — +? > OUT (17)

2 Find the missing number.   **Example**

 = ⬛ 3 × 1 pound

a
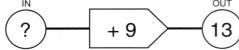 = ☐ × 5 pence

b
 = ☐ × 20 pence

c
 = ☐ × 5 pence + ☐ × 20 pence

3 Here are some simple number patterns.
Find the next two numbers in each.
a 2, 4, 6, 8, ☐, ☐   **b** 1, 3, 5, 7, ☐, ☐   **c** 0, 4, 8, 12, ☐, ☐   **d** 5, 10, 15, 20, ☐, ☐

4 Work out the number under the finger.

a 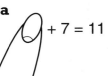 + 7 = 11   **b** 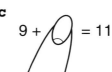 − 3 = 4   **c** 9 + 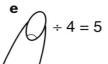 = 11

d × 3 = 21   **e**  ÷ 4 = 5   **f** 18 ÷ 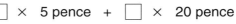 = 3

Simple Number Patterns

 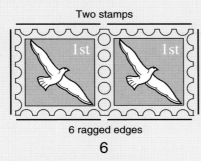 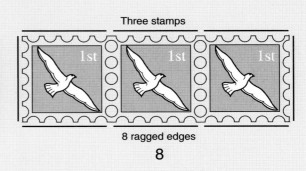

One stamp	Two stamps	Three stamps
4 ragged edges	6 ragged edges	8 ragged edges
4	6	8

4, 6, 8, ... the list goes up in twos.
The next three numbers are: 10, 12, 14.

EXERCISE 1

1 Find the next two numbers in these number patterns.

   a 1, 4, 7, 10, 13, □, □   **b** 2, 12, 22, 32, 42, □, □   **c** 1, 7, 13, 19, □, □
   d 3, 6, 9, 12, 15, □, □   **e** 6, 12, 18, 24, □, □   **f** 10, 21, 32, 43, □, □

2 Here are some not so simple patterns.
Can you find the next two numbers for each?

   a $\frac{1}{2}, \frac{1}{3}, \frac{1}{4}, \frac{1}{5}$, □, □   **b** 10 000, 1000, 100, □, □

   c 100, 94, 88, 82, □, □   **d** $1 \times 2 = 2, 2 \times 3 = 6, 3 \times 4 = 12$, □, □

   e $3 \times 1, 5 \times 2, 7 \times 3$, □, □   **f** 100, 99, 97, 94, □, □

3 The **triangular** numbers

   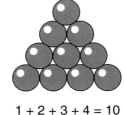

    1   1 + 2 = 3   1 + 2 + 3 = 6   1 + 2 + 3 + 4 = 10

1, 3, 6 and 10 are called triangular numbers.
Make diagrams to help you find the next two triangular numbers.

4 The **square** numbers

  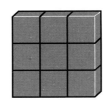 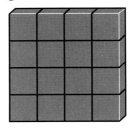

   1 × 1 = 1   2 × 2 = 4   3 × 3 = 9   4 × 4 = 16

1, 4, 9 and 16 are called square numbers.
Make diagrams to help you find the next two square numbers.

Using Letters

 + 7 = 8

It is often easier to use a letter rather than a
finger to stand for an unknown number.

$x + 7 = 8$

EXERCISE 2

1 Each set of cards adds up to 21.
What value has the card marked x in each case?

a 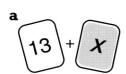 **b** 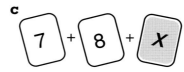 **c** 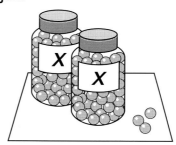 **d**

2 Emily puts the same number of marbles into each jar.
We don't know how many.
We'll say there are x marbles in each jar.

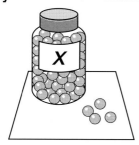

So this picture shows $x + 4$ marbles and this is $2x + 3$ marbles.

How many marbles are in each picture below?

a 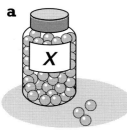 **b**  **c**

3 Tom puts 6 matches into each box.
So he needs $4 \times 6 = 24$ matches.

Copy and complete these sentences.
a Sal puts 7 matches into each box.
So she needs $4 \times \boxed{} = \boxed{}$ matches.
b Mac puts 9 matches into each box.
So he needs $4 \times \boxed{} = \boxed{}$ matches.
c Val puts x matches into each box.
So she needs $4 \times \boxed{} = \boxed{}$ matches.

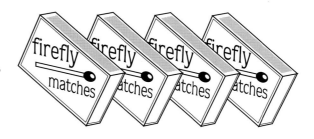

4

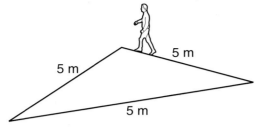
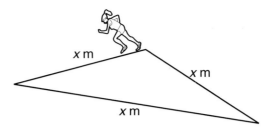

The perimeter of the triangle is
$5 + 5 + 5 = 15$ metres
or $3 \times 5 = 15$ metres.

The perimeter of the triangle is
$x + x + x = 3x$ metres
or $3 \times x = 3x$ metres.

Work out the perimeters of these shapes in metres.

a

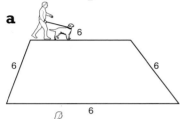

b

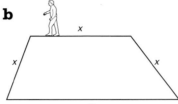

c

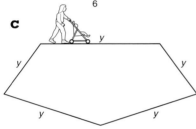

d

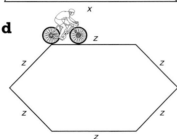

5

| From Galashiels to Paisley is 140 km. John has done 80 km. He still has **140 – 80** = 60 km to go. | From Galashiels to Troon is x km. Mike has done 80 km. He still has **x – 80** km to go. |

How far has each traveller still to go?

a

b

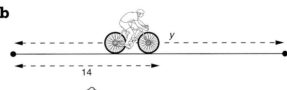

c

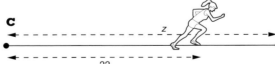

Be careful with the subtraction now.

d

e

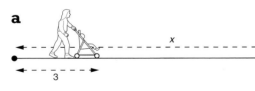

f

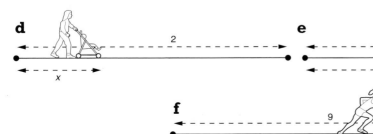

Letters for Numbers

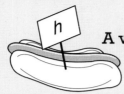

A hotdog costs *h* pence.
A veggieburger costs *v* pence.

Here are some examples of how things can be simplified or tidied up.

$h + h + h = 3h$

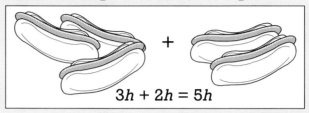

$3h + 2h = 5h$

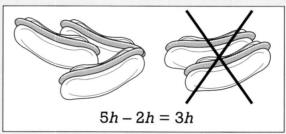

$5h - 2h = 3h$

EXERCISE 3

1 Tidy up the following.

a $a + a$	**b** $x + x + x$	**c** $t + t + t + t$	**d** $2y + 4y$
e $4a + 5a$	**f** $3x - 2x$	**g** $8d + 3d$	**h** $9b - 2b$
i $c + 2c + 3c$	**j** $4a + a + 3a$	**k** $2h + h + 4h$	**l** $3y + 6y + 7y$
m $5a - a + 2a$	**n** $4t + 4t - 6t$	**o** $m + 5m - 4m$	**p** $3x - 2x - x$

Here are some more examples.

$h + 3v + 2h + 2v$
$= 3h + 5v$

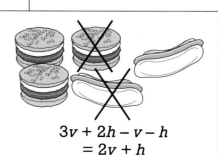

$3v + 2h - v - h$
$= 2v + h$

2 Simplify the following.

a $a + 5a + 2b + 3b$ **b** $3m + m + n + 2n$ **c** $2x + 3x + 4y + y$
d $3d - d + 4e - 2e$ **e** $4v - 2v + 3w - 2w$ **f** $8a - 3a + 6b - 4b$
g $x + y + x + y$ **h** $2a + b + 2a + b$ **i** $4m + 3n + 2n + m$
j $4b + 6c - b - 3c$ **k** $8x + 3y - 5x - y$ **l** $3a + 7b - 6b - a$

> **Examples**
>
> $4 \times x = 4x$ $x \times 4 = 4x$ (Put the number first.)
> $x \times y = xy$ $b \times a \times c = abc$ (Arrange alphabetically.)
> $a \times a = aa = a^2$ $b \times b \times b = bbb = b^3$

3 Simplify the following.

a $3 \times y$ **b** $5 \times b$ **c** $a \times 4$ **d** $d \times 7$
e $c \times d$ **f** $x \times y$ **g** $b \times a$ **h** $d \times c$
i $b \times d \times c$ **j** $c \times b \times a$ **k** $5 \times a \times b$ **l** $7 \times m \times n$
m $6 \times c \times b$ **n** $3 \times q \times p$ **o** $b \times a \times 5$ **p** $d \times c \times 3 \times e$
q $t \times m \times h$ **r** $m \times y \times d$ **s** $a \times c \times 4 \times b$ **t** $b \times b$
u $n \times n$ **v** $m \times m \times m$ **w** $y \times y \times y \times y \times y$ **x** $a \times a \times b \times b$

Swopping Letters for Numbers

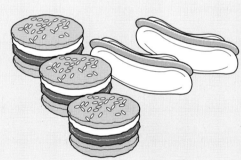

Here is an order which will cost $3v + 2h$.
If we are told a veggieburger costs £1
     $v = 1$
and a hotdog costs £2
     $h = 2$
we can work out the bill:
     $3v + 2h$
     $= 3 \times v + 2 \times h$
     $= 3 \times 1 + 2 \times 2$
     $= 3 + 4$
     $= 7.$

EXERCISE 4

1

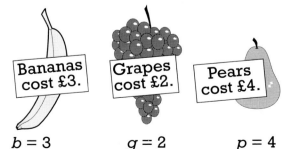

Bananas cost £3.
Grapes cost £2.
Pears cost £4.

$b = 3$ $g = 2$ $p = 4$

Work out the cost of each order.

a $3p$ **b** $b + g$
c $2b + g$ **d** $3p + 2b + 2g$
e $2g + 3p + 2b$

2 For $a = 5$ and $b = 3$, work out:
   a $a + b$ **b** $a - b$ **c** ab **d** $2a$ **e** $6b$ **f** $2ab$

3 For $m = 4$ and $n = 7$, work out:

    a $m + n$ **b** $n - m$ **c** mn **d** $2m$ **e** $3n$ **f** m^2

4

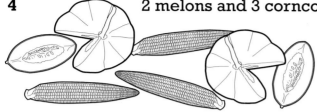

2 melons and 3 corncobs cost $2m + 3c$.

Work out the bill if:

    a $m = 2$ and $c = 1$
    b $m = 3$ and $c = 2$
    c $m = 1$ and $c = 3$
    d $m = 4$ and $c = 4$

5 For $c = 4$, $d = 1$ and $e = 6$, work out:

a $c + d + e$	**b** cd	**c** ce	**d** de	**e** cde	**f** $c - d$
g $e - c$	**h** $2c$	**i** $3d$	**j** $5e$	**k** $2c + 3d$	**l** $3c + e$
m $2e - d$	**n** $2d + 2c$	**o** $3c - 2e$	**p** $3de$	**q** d^2	**r** c^3

Equations

Example 1 What number is under the finger? 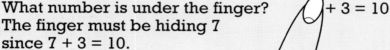$+ 3 = 10$
The finger must be hiding 7
since $7 + 3 = 10$.

Example 2 $x + 3 = 10$ (using x instead of a finger)
           $x = 7$ (since $7 + 3 = 10$)

Example 3 $2x = 10$ (means $2 \times x = 10$)
           $x = 5$ (since $2 \times 5 = 10$)

EXERCISE 5

1 Say which number is under each finger.

    a $+ 4 = 11$ **b** $+ 1 = 5$ **c** $- 2 = 8$ **d** $- 3 = 12$

    e $3 +$ $= 13$ **f** $7 +$ $= 9$ **g** $8 -$ $= 1$ **h** $7 -$ $= 2$

2 Find the unknown numbers in these equations.

a $x + 7 = 11$	**b** $x + 1 = 5$	**c** $4 + x = 9$	**d** $8 + x = 11$
e $2 + a = 6$	**f** $10 + a = 15$	**g** $6 - a = 5$	**h** $10 - a = 8$
i $9 - y = 3$	**j** $y - 1 = 2$	**k** $y - 2 = 3$	**l** $y - 8 = 2$
m $x - 6 = 12$	**n** $x + 2 = 2$	**o** $x - 5 = 0$	**p** $x - 10 = 9$

3 Say which number is under each finger.

a $2 \times$ 🖐 $= 8$ **b** $3 \times$ 🖐 $= 12$ **c** $4 \times$ 🖐 $= 20$ **d** $5 \times$ 🖐 $= 10$

e $3 \times$ 🖐 $= 15$ **f** $6 \times$ 🖐 $= 24$ **g** $5 \times$ 🖐 $= 35$ **h** $7 \times$ 🖐 $= 14$

4 Find the unknown numbers in these equations.

a $2x = 6$	**b** $3x = 12$	**c** $5x = 10$	**d** $8x = 24$
e $3a = 15$	**f** $4a = 16$	**g** $6a = 30$	**h** $7a = 14$
i $5y = 50$	**j** $2y = 0$	**k** $8y = 0$	**l** $10y = 10$
m $2x = 50$	**n** $3x = 18$	**o** $5x = 40$	**p** $4x = 36$

Formulae

Double-glazing is being put into the front windows of the houses in an estate.

The number of windows needed
is **four times**
the number of houses.

Houses ─ $\times 4$ ─ Windows

Example For 2 houses we need $2 \times 4 = 8$ windows.

EXERCISE 6

1 Use the formula above to work out the number of windows needed for:

    a 3 houses   **b** 5 houses   **c** 6 houses   **d** 10 houses.

2

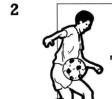

FIVE-A-SIDE COMPETITION
The number of players
is **five times**
the number of teams.

Use the formula to find out the number of players if there are:

a 4 teams   **b** 8 teams   **c** 16 teams.

3 The stand is full for the big match.

Use the formula to work out the
number of spectators if the stand has:

a 8 rows **b** 10 rows **c** 12 rows.

The number of spectators
is **twelve times**
the number of rows of seats.

4

The number
of Rollies
is **nine times**
the number
of packets.

Use the formula to work out the number of
Rollies in:

a 3 packets **b** 8 packets **c** 12 packets.

5 Bert's wheelbarrow can hold
3 concrete slabs.
He wants to move a number of slabs
to his back garden.

The number of journeys
is **one third**
the number of slabs.

Use the formula to find the number
of journeys he'll need if there are:

a 12 slabs **b** 30 slabs **c** 45 slabs **d** 27 slabs.

6 Mr Tapp, the plumber, calculates his charges using this formula.

The number of hours
times 10
plus 15
gives cost in £.

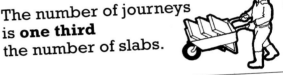

Calculate his charge for a job lasting:

a 1 hour **b** 4 hours **c** 7 hours.

7 Sparks Electricity plc charges using this formula.

The number of units
times 0.1
plus 10
gives charge in £.

Calculate how much they charge a
customer who uses:

a 100 units **b** 1000 units
c 750 units **d** 643 units.

8 Rent-a-Car charges for car hire using this formula.

De-Luxe Hire charges using this formula.

a Copy and complete this table.

Charge (£)	1 day	2 days	3 days	4 days	5 days	6 days
Rent-a-Car	18	26				
De-Luxe Hire	21					

b Which company is cheaper? Write a sentence to explain your answer.

Making Formulae

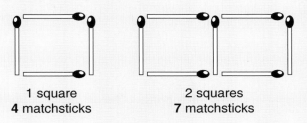

1 square
4 matchsticks

2 squares
7 matchsticks

3 squares
10 matchsticks

4, 7, 10, ... The number of sticks goes up by **3** each time.
We expect the **three times** table.
The first number, **4**, is 1 more than 3.
We then expect to **add 1**.

Check that this formula works.

> The number of squares
> **times 3 then add 1**
> gives the number of sticks.

EXERCISE 7

1 The table shows how Jill's sunflower has started to grow.

Age in weeks	1	2	3	4	5	6
Height in cm	5	6	7			

Assume the pattern continues.

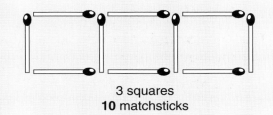

Age in weeks
add ......
gives the height in cm.

a Copy and complete the table.
b Write down a formula for calculating the height of the sunflower given its age.
c How tall is Jill's sunflower after ten weeks?

2 Sophie makes pearl earrings.
These sketches show the first three sizes.

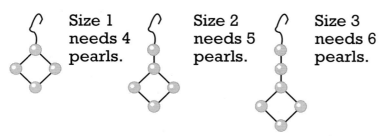

Size 1 needs 4 pearls.

Size 2 needs 5 pearls.

Size 3 needs 6 pearls.

a Draw a sketch to show the size 4 earring.

b Copy and complete the table.

Size number	1	2	3	4	5	6
Number of pearls	4	5				

c Write down a rule for finding the number of pearls needed given the size number.

d The largest size Sophie makes is size 10. How many pearls will this need?

Size number
add ......
gives the number of pearls.

3 The growth of a grass plant over three weeks is shown in these sketches.

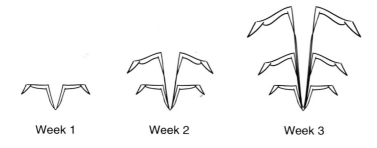

Week 1   Week 2   Week 3

a Draw a sketch to show what the plant will look like after week 4.

b Copy and complete the table.

Week	1	2	3	4	5	6		10
Number of leaves	2	4						

c Write down a rule for finding the number of leaves if you know the number of weeks.

4 Lite-the-Nite plc makes display signs.
They make different sizes of letters
which need different numbers of bulbs.
The number of bulbs used in different
sizes of the letter L is shown below.

Lite-the-nite
HOTEL
Let us focus on you

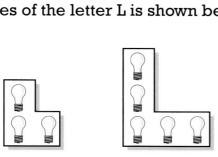

Size 1   Size 2   Size 3

a Draw a sketch to show the pattern of the bulbs needed in a size 4 letter L.
b Copy and complete the table.

Size of letter L	1	2	3	4	5	6		10
Number of bulbs	3							

c Write down a rule for finding the number of bulbs needed if the size
number is known.

5 The number of bulbs used to make different sizes of the letter T is shown below.

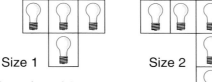

Size 1   Size 2   Size 3

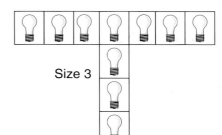

a Sketch the size 4 letter T.
b Copy and complete the table.

Size of letter T	1	2	3	4	5	6		10
Number of bulbs	4							

c Write down the rule for finding the number of bulbs
if the size number is known.

6 A star sign
is planned.

Size 1

Size 2

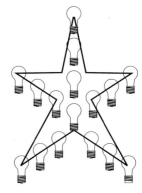

Size 3

Work out the rule for finding the number of bulbs if the size number is known.

CHECK-UP ON ALGEBRA

1 Find the next two numbers in these number patterns.
  a 2, 8, 14, 20, ...   **b** 53, 49, 45, 41, ...

2 Archie walked 4 kilometres and then a further d kilometres.
  How many kilometres did he walk in total?

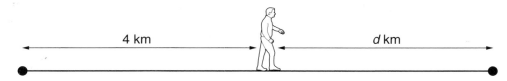

4 km d km

3 Simplify the following.
  a $3y + 4y + 5y$ **b** $5x - x$ **c** $a + 3b + 2a - b$
  d $n \times 2 \times m$ **e** $a \times a \times a \times a$ **f** $2 \times y \times 3 \times y$

4 $u = 3$, $v = 4$ and $w = 5$.
  Calculate:
  a $u + v + w$ **b** uv **c** $4w$ **d** $3u - 2v$

5 Find the unknown numbers in these equations.
  a $x + 6 = 11$ **b** $4 - a = 1$ **c** $y - 7 = 3$ **d** $b - 3 = 3$
  e $9 + m = 9$ **f** $7m = 21$ **g** $3x = 3$ **h** $4x = 12$

6 Mail Order Sweaters charge
  using this formula.

> The number of sweaters
> **times 25 plus 3**
> gives the cost in £.

  a Why do you think the 3 is added on?
  b How much is charged for:
    (i) 2 sweaters   (ii) 3 sweaters   (iii) 5 sweaters?

7 Sophie now makes a new type of pearl earring.
  The first three sizes are shown below.

Size 1

Size 2

Size 3

  a Make a sketch of what you think
    the size 4 earring looks like.
  b Copy and complete the table.
  c Write down a formula for finding
    the number of pearls needed if
    the size is known.
  d The largest size Sophie makes is
    size 10. How many pearls are
    needed?

Size number	1	2	3	4	5	6
Number of pearls	3					